THE
BASEBALL
TRIVIA QUIZ BOOK

FROM

JELL-O® BRAND
Pudding
Pops®
FROZEN PUDDING
ON A STICK

By
C. M. Howard

VENTURA BOOKS
New York City
Printed in the United States
All Rights Reserved

Ventura Associates, Inc.
200 Madison Avenue/New York, 10016

Contents

	Introduction	7
I.	Facts, Founders and Firsts	9
	Quiz	14
	Answers	20
II.	Sluggers, Swingers and Superstars	35
	Quiz	37
	Answers	43
III.	The Men on the Mound	57
	Quiz	59
	Answers	67
IV.	Runners, Fielders and other Strangers	87
	Quiz	89
	Answers	93
V.	Great Managers and Great Teams	103
	Quiz	105
	Answers	111
VI.	The World Series	125
	Quiz	127
	Answers	130
	Great Moments in World Series History Quiz	137
	Answers	145
	World Series Results 1903-1983	150
VII.	One for the Record Books	157
	The Statistics Game	159
	Answers	165
VIII.	Know the Rules	169
	Rulebook Quiz	170
	Answers	172

Introduction

Most boys grow up with the name and batting average of their favorite ballplayer indelibly marked on their memories. What's more important to a growing youth—the Gettysburg Address or the Babe's farewell address? Not even the names of presidents, the geography of Europe, nor the square root tables can rival baseball facts for position in their minds and imaginations. The history of America's favorite pastime is better read, memorized and digested than America's history itself. Most boys know about Babe Ruth's famous called shot. They know that a West Point cadet named Abner Doubleday invented the game in Cooperstown, New York. They know that Jackie Robinson, famed second baseman for the Brooklyn Dodgers, was the first Black baseball player to play in the major leagues.

Unfortunately, none of these are true.

The history of baseball has become confused by

thousands of colorful legends and myths that have sprouted from the imaginations of sportswriters, fans, promoters and the baseball players themselves. The history of the game has been exaggerated and twisted. Stories about even the most colorful stars have been stretched beyond recognition. Even the most educated broadcaster, the most diehard fan might no longer know the truth —that the designated hitter rule was not a product of the 1970s, that the first World Series game was not lost by a team ironically named the New York Mets, and so on.

To truly understand the history of the game and the stars and teams that have made baseball what it is today, one must first strip away the legends. Only then can one understand how closely the history of the game has paralleled the history of the last hundred years in the United States. Babe Ruth did not call his shot. Abner Doubleday did not invent baseball. Jackie Robinson was not the first Black ballplayer in the major leagues. Only then can one understand that the sport wasn't always a multibillion dollar industry, that scoreboards weren't always electronic, that ballplayers didn't always play for million dollar sums while wearing double-knits. Baseball has had its share of scandals, financial worries, ups and downs and rowdy stars. The true story of our national pastime is even more exciting than the myths.

Chapter One

Facts, Founders and Firsts

Before we begin asking some of the harder questions about the history of baseball, we might as well clear the air about the most basic trivia question of all. Who invented baseball?

Oddly enough it wasn't until the early part of the twentieth century, when the game was first establishing itself as both a financially successful entertainment as well as our nation's favorite pastime, that questions first arose concerning the origins and history of the game. To most the question didn't even seem very important; all that mattered was that anywhere you looked, back in those days, you would find both boys and men picking up games, slugging, running and fielding.

After years of blind acceptance that the game was native to the United States, many critics chose to prove that, in fact, baseball had European origins and was a copy of many traditional and ancient ball and bat games. On the other hand, many defenders of the American theory of the game arose to prove that, in fact, baseball was a strictly American invention with no ties to earlier European games.

Albert G. Spalding, founder of the famed sporting goods company that has manufactured baseballs and baseball equipment since the establishment of the game, was the leading advocate of the American sport school of thought. Leading the attack against Spalding and other supporters of this theory was an English-born sportswriter named Henry Chadwick, who claimed that there were many similarities between baseball and the game known as rounders, which he had played as a young boy back in England.

Spalding, who also owned the Chicago White Sox, obviously had a lot to gain from being proven correct. If it were proven that baseball was an American game through and through, the sport would take off even more than it already had, and Spalding would benefit financially. Remember, those were the days when America was first emerging as a major international power. The Spanish-American War was just over; America was racing to make up for lost time in the international colonial scramble. Certainly if Spalding could prove that baseball were red, white and blue, the game would flourish and so would his investments.

Chadwick, who is officially credited with inventing the box score, claimed that the main difference between rounders and baseball was the shape of the field and the method of putting a runner out. He explained that the rules of baseball, established by the Knickerbocker Base Ball Club in 1845, changed the infield from a square to a diamond and had substituted simply throwing the ball at the runner to touching the runner to make the out. Chadwick was convinced that these were the only significant differences between baseball and rounders and was set on proving his point.

In order to settle their dispute once and for all, both parties agreed to let an official governmental agency investigate the problem. As a result a high-level commission was founded in 1904, including U.S. senators, judges, historians, and baseball experts, instructed to investigate the origins of the game.

Spalding issued the commission a lengthy and influential paper maintaining that baseball was derived from a colonial day game known as "One Old Cat," which had three players: a batter, a catcher and a thrower. This, Spalding asserted, evolved into a game that was known as "Town Ball," which later became known as baseball after Major General Abner Doubleday, then a cadet at West Point, invented the game in his hometown of Cooperstown, New York in the spring of 1839. In addition, Spalding claimed to have spoken to a playmate of Doubleday's, Abner Graves, who was willing to testify that during that spring of 1839 he saw Abner Doubleday outline the first baseball diamond in the dirt in Cooperstown, and played with him and other town boys in the first and historic baseball contest.

Spalding also added in his report that "I am

strongly inclined to the belief that Cooperstown, New York is the birthplace of the present American game of baseball, and that Major General Abner Doubleday was the originator of the game. It certainly appeals to an American's pride to have had the great national game of base ball created and named by a major general of the United States Army . . ."

Although it was later shown that Doubleday wasn't even in Cooperstown during that time and that Abner Graves might have been paid off to lie, the specially formed baseball commission finally put the question to rest in 1907, siding with Spalding and his Doubleday thesis. Although there was much doubt as to the documentary evidence the commission had accumulated during its three years of investigation, it was their decision that began the traditional story of the invention of the game. Although further evidence has since discounted the Abner Doubleday story, the state of New York still maintains that Cooperstown is the birthplace of baseball, and the U.S. Congress in 1952 maintained that baseball is a native American sport.

These are the beginnings of the game, caught up in controversy and confusion from the very start. What about the rest of the history of the game? Can it possibly be as confused and convoluted as this story?

The history of baseball is an exciting one, containing many such controversies and an equal number of exciting characters and historical events. The following trivia quiz will test your knowledge of the early history of the game and of important landmarks in the game's development. Be careful; the questions are not always as simple and straightforward as they might seem. Try to remember all those facts and figures that you've got stored away in the back of your memory along with your childhood dreams of someday being a great ballplayer yourself. If you need some help, dig out that shoebox full of baseball cards you've saved in your hall closet. Only the true baseball scholars will know all the answers.

Facts, Founders and First Quiz

1. Besides the fictitious founding of the game of baseball, with what famed historical event is Major General Abner Doubleday credited?

2. What was the Knickerbocker Base Ball Club of New York?

3. What were the teams to play the first organized baseball game and where was the game played?

4. Who was the first radio announcer to call a live broadcast from a World Series game and how was that broadcast transmitted?

5. What was the first intercollegiate baseball game and where was it played?

6. What was the final score of that game?

7. What was the first team to wear baseball uniforms?

8. What were these uniforms made of?

9. Who was the father of organized baseball?

10. What were the dimensions of the first baseball diamond and how have these dimensions since changed?

11. What were the original positions set down for the field in a professional baseball game?

12. What was the longest night game in recorded

baseball history and where was it played?

13. What was the longest game in the history of the game?

14. When was the first official night game and why was the night game first instituted?

15. What was the first professional baseball team and how are they credited with spreading the popularity of professional baseball as a spectator sport?

16. Who was the gambler who fixed the notorious Black Sox Scandal during the 1919 World Series?

17. What were the eight players exposed as involved with being paid to throw the 1919 World Series?

18. Who was the first commissioner of baseball and how did he first reach national acclaim before being appointed to this position?

19. How were the eight convicted Black Sox punished?

20. When was the first ladies day game and where was it first played?

21. What were the first ten teams that banded together to form the first baseball league, and what was that league officially called?

22. Why did this first baseball league flounder and finally dissolve?

23. In Ebbets Field in Brooklyn in 1924, a stadium that could only accommodate at most 30,000 spectators was jammed with 50,000. What happened?

24. Who was the first president to begin the tradition of throwing out the first season's ball?

25. What were the provisions of the first reserve clause and why was the clause first written?

26. What trade caused Curt Flood to sue the sport of baseball over the reserve clause?

27. What baseball league was formed in reaction to the institution of the reserve clause?

28. What was the longest double-header in the history of baseball?

29. Who wore the first baseball glove?

30. Who were the millionaires who founded the Mexican League?

31. What American baseball players were lured down to Mexico in 1946 to play in the newly formed and soon to be defunct Mexican League?

32. Who was offered the chance to be the first president of the Mexican League?

33. What team began the major leagues' westward expansion and in what year did it begin?

34. What was that team's attendance the year before and the year after it moved westward?

35. Who invented the designated hitter ruling and why wasn't it instituted until the 1973 season in the American League?

36. Who was the first baseball player to walk on the field wearing a number on his uniform?

37. Who was the first professional ballplayer to earn $100,000 a year playing for a major league team?

38. What was that player's record during that season he was first offered this salary?

39. In 1969 the first American League Championship Series was played between what two teams?

16

40. What year was the ground-rule double ruling instituted?

41. Who was the first Black ballplayer to play in the major leagues and for what team did he play?

42. Who were the first Black ballplayers to play in the American League and for what teams did they play?

43. What were their records?

44. When was the first World Series held and what were the two teams?

45. What were the results of the first World Series?

46. Which pitcher was most responsible for the victory?

47. What stadium is considered to have been the first modern stadium?

48. Who was the first batter to hit a home run in the Astrodome?

49. When was the first All-Star game played?

50. What was the first baseball game played on artificial turf?

51. Which players have won the Most Valuable Player (MVP) award three times?

52. What was the impact of the Continental League and who was the league's major backer?

53. Who is credited with the founding of the National League and upon what premise was the new league founded?

54. What year and what team brought baseball into a new and international arena?

55. What was the Landis-Eastman Agreement?

56. Who were the first five players to be inducted into the Baseball Hall of Fame in Cooperstown,

New York?

57. What was the Union Association?

58. In 1969 who was chosen as the greatest All-Time player and who was chosen as the greatest living player?

59. What was the cause of the 1969 spring training boycott?

60. What were the occupations of the members of the first professional baseball team and what were their salaries for the first season?

61. How long did the original game of baseball last?

62. What was the American League originally called?

63. While World War I caused an early curtailment of the 1918 season, what effect did World War II have on the sport?

64. In 1973 it was ruled that no player who had been in baseball for ten years and with the same team for the last five, could be traded without his approval. Which player took advantage of this ruling at its inception?

65. Which team is owned by the president of a hamburger company?

66. Who was the founder and first president of the American League?

67. Why was an early Cincinnati team expelled from the National League?

68. What year did the Giants and Dodgers move from New York to California?

69. Who was the manager of the first professional baseball team?

70. What newspaper had the first sports page?

71. In 1884 which cities were the homes of Union Association teams?

72. What baseball promoter took his team on a barnstorming tour around the world in the late nineteenth century?

73. When was baseball first introduced to Hawaii?

74. What great first baseman will never enter the Hall of Fame because of suspected irregularities in his play?

75. During what year was no All-Star game played?

76. When was the American League started?

77. Who was one of the first umpires and is considered the greatest umpire of all times?

78. Who was one of the famous early pitchers who was generally known as the "Iron Man" and for how many years did he pitch?

79. Who won 40 games for the White Sox in 1908?

80. When was the split up of Major League baseball into eastern and western divisions?

81. When was the first baseball strike?

82. When was the last strike?

83. What were the dates the strike in 1981 started and finished?

Answers

1. Abner Doubleday's most significant contribution to history, other than his fictitious credit for inventing the game of baseball, is that he commanded the regiment that fired the first shots on Fort Sumter during the Civil War. Until Albert Spalding mentioned his name in connection with the invention of baseball this was considered his only significant historical contribution. There is no mention of baseball in any local Cooperstown historical writings nor in any of Doubleday's letters.

2. Organized as a gentleman's social and fraternal organization, The Knickerbocker Base Ball Club of New York is commonly recognized as being the first organized baseball team, having its origins in the early part of 1842. Although there are recorded to have been earlier town ball clubs, it was the Knickerbocker Club that drew up the rules that have since been passed on as those which designed the present-day sport.

3. The first organized baseball game was played between the Knickerbocker Base Ball Club and the New York Base Ball Club on June 19, 1846 at the Elysian Fields in Hoboken, New Jersey. The record book for this game reveals that the Knickerbockers were severely beaten during the first contest by a final score of 32-1.

4. Grantland Rice, the immortal sports editor of the *New York Tribune,* called the first game of the 1922 World Series between the New York Giants and the New York Yankees, making it the first time a championship game was called live for the radio audience. Rice's play-by-play announcements were broadcast via radiophone to an estimated one million people within 199 miles of the metropolitan New York area.

5. The country's first intercollegiate game is recorded to have been played between Amherst and Williams College on July 1, 1859 in Pittsfield, Massachusetts. Both teams were chosen by lottery from each school's enrollment.

6. The final outcome of this historical intercollegiate confrontation was Amherst 73, Williams 32. It had been a close battle until the fourth inning, when Amherst collected most of its runs.

7. The New York Knickerbockers startled the baseball world when they walked out on the field wearing consistent uniforms during the first game of the 1851 season.

8. The Knickerbocker uniforms were composed of navy blue pants, belts, white shirts and straw hats. It wasn't until a few years later that the team adopted a smaller, less cumbersome cricket-like cap. Although the uniforms were uncomfortable, it wasn't until 1868 that any changes were made. In that year the Cincinnati Red Stockings walked on the field wearing knickers (actually cut-

down pants).

9.   Alexander Cartwright, a 25-year-old civil engineer, is undisputedly given the title of father of organized baseball. It was Cartwright, founder of The Knickerbocker Base Ball Club of New York, who set down standard dimensions, positions, conduct and etiquette for the early game of baseball.

10.   The dimensions of the first baseball diamond, designed by Cartwright in 1845, basically still stand today. There are 90 feet between all the bags. Cartwright's design called for the distance between the pitcher and batter to be only 45 feet. This dimension has since been changed to 60 feet, 6 inches, as it stands today.

11.   Cartwright also set up the standard positions, for a baseball fielding team. This too has basically remained the same. Differences arise only in that the shortstop in Cartwright's day stood in front of the baseline and the catcher stood far back behind the plate.

12.   The longest night game in recorded history was between St. Louis and the New York Mets, lasting 7 hours and 4 minutes on September 11, 1974.

13.   The longest game in the history of the game was a 26-inning thriller between the Boston Braves and the Brooklyn Dodgers on May 1, 1920; it ended in a 1-1 tie.

14.   The first official night game was played on May 24, 1935 in Cincinnati before a crowd of 20,000 fans. President Franklin D. Roosevelt pressed a button in the White House that

illuminated the stadium for this historic event. The experiment was primarily done by the Red's management as a means to boost attendance.

15. The Cincinnati Red Stockings, first organized in 1866, was the first professional baseball team. Beginning in 1866 as a semiprofessional team, paying only four of the team members a minimal salary, the team eventually turned totally professional in 1869 by paying all the team members a salary. The Red Stockings went on from these origins to play for two full years of undefeated play. The team won a total of 130 games and tied only one. It was this team that set the example for other professional teams and led to the general improvement in the quality of the game.

16. The gambler credited with the rigging of the 1919 World Series between the Chicago White Sox and Cincinnati Reds was the New York gambler Arnold Rothstein. Information gathered by the state attorney's office indicated that Rothstein's bets had won him between $300,000 and $400,000. Other gamblers reportedly involved were Sport Sullivan, Abe Attel, Nat Evans, Hal Chase, Sleepy Billy Burns and Billy Maharag.

17. The eight ballplayers who were bribed to throw the 1919 World Series were Joe Jackson, Buck Weaver, Fred McMullin, Claude Williams, Swede Riseberg, Hap Felsch, Eddie Cicotte, and Chick Gandil. The players were payed between $5,000 (paid to Shoeless Joe Jackson) and a walloping $10,000 (paid to Eddie Cicotte, the White Sox star hurler).

18. The first commissioner of baseball was Judge Kenesaw Mountain Landis, who was elected in November of 1920 following the Black Sox scandal. Landis had gained his reputation as a hardened justice while a federal court judge in northern Illinois, where he had been appointed by President Theodore Roosevelt in 1905.

19. Landis banished the eight players from the game, claiming that "regardless of the verdict of juries . . . no player who throws a game, no player that undertakes or promises to throw a game, no player who sits in conference with a bunch of crooks and gamblers where the means of throwing games are discussed and who does not promptly tell his club about it, will ever play professional baseball again . . ."

20. The first official ladies day game was held on June 16, 1883 in a game between the New York Giants and the Cleveland Indians at the Polo Grounds in New York. Later, in 1912, the St. Louis Browns initiated a ladies day game but made sure that all ladies were accompanied by a male escort. The special feature didn't become a regular event until Branch Rickey took over the St. Louis club in 1917.

21. Founded on March 4, 1871, the National Association of Baseball Players was organized in New York, bringing together the following ten professional teams: the New York Mutuals, the Chicago White Stockings, the Washington Olympics, the Troy Haymakers, the Philadelphia Athletics, the Cleveland Forest City Club, the Fort Wayne Kekiongas, the Rockford Forest City Club, the Bostons and the Eckford Club of Brooklyn.

22. The first association was doomed from the start because the players did little to regulate the conduct of their fellow players. The games themselves became rowdy displays. Drunken brawls, betting and the fixing of games was as common as contract breaking, team jumping and, oh yes, hitting, running and fielding.

23. It was on September 7, 1924 that all of Brooklyn came out to watch and root for their favorite sons against the hometown rivals, the New York Giants. The Giants and Dodgers were neck and neck for the National League pennant and if the Dodgers pulled off this big one they would be in first place, The game had been sold out days ahead of time, but that didn't stop the crowds from coming. As many as 100,000 people surrounded the stadium before game time. Then pandemonium and the first baseball riot broke out. An estimated 50,000 packed Ebbets Field just to watch the Giants beat the home team in a tight battle, 8-7.

24. President William Howard Taft began this springtime tradition at the beginning of the 1910 season in Washington, D.C. The date was June 9, 1910.

25. The now infamous reserve clause was first devised at a meeting held in Buffalo, New York in September, 1879, at which time team owners made a secret pact to retain five players and keep them off the National League player market. The other team owners agreed not to employ these reserved players nor to play a game against any team that violated the pact. The reserve clause, it was believed, was designed to keep the Chicago club, the richest one in the league, from holding a monopoly on the sport.

26. Flood challenged the reserve clause after his trade by the St. Louis Cardinals to the Philadelphia Phillies in 1970.

27. In 1885, in reaction to the reserve clause, the National Brotherhood of Baseball Players was formed. This new league drew players dissatisfied with the reserve clause ruling, but eventually dissolved due to lack of public support in 1890.

28. The longest double-header in the history of the game took place on May 31, 1964 at Shea Stadium in New York, between the New York Mets and San Francisco Giants. The first game had been a routine Giant win, 5-3. The second game went for 23 innings and ended with an 8-6 Giant victory at 11:30 that night. When the first game began 57,000 fans had packed the stadium, but when the second game ended nine hours and fifty-two minutes later, only 15,000 diehard fans were still present.

29. The first baseball glove, according to Albert Spalding, was worn by a fellow named Charles C. Waitt from Boston in or around 1875. The glove Spalding described seeing Waitt wearing was a flesh-colored, thin glove with a round opening in the back. Spalding added that neither he nor any other player playing organized ball began wearing a glove until 1877.

30. In 1946 Jorge Pasquel and his four brothers, a group of multimillionaire Mexicans, decided to try to bring baseball to Mexico City by luring big-name American ballplayers south of the border with promises of large bonuses and five- and six-figure salaries. The league folded after losing $400,000 in 1948.

31. Pasquel snagged the following players: Danny Gardella, Roy Zimmerman, Nap Reyes and Sal Maglie from the New York Giants; Mickey Owens from the Brooklyn Dodgers; Roberto Ortiz and Chile Gomez from the Washington Senators; Roberto Estailla from the Philadelphia Athletics; Alex Carresquel from the Chicago White Sox; and Harry Feldom and Ace Adoms, both pitchers from the New York Giants. The St. Louis Cardinals lost an estimated $200,000 worth of ballplayers. Players that weren't attacked despite enormous salary pledges were Hank Greenberg, who was offered a three-year salary of $360,000; Bob Feller, who was offered a three-year salary of $500,000; and Pete Reiser.

32. The Pasquel brothers offered Babe Ruth $1,000,000 to become the league's first president.

33. The map of professional baseball in the United States spread westward when in 1952 the Boston Braves moved to Milwaukee. The move was unprecedented in the history of the game.

34. The Braves' attendance that season in Milwaukee was astounding. Their attendance in 13 games was as high as 302,667, more than they had drawn the entire previous season in Boston. They ended the season with the highest attendance in National League history: 1,826,3897.

35. The designated hitter ruling was first suggested as far back as 1928 by John Heydler, then

National League president. It didn't come into effect until the American League recognized the value of hitting as a means of boosting excitement in the game 45 years later, in 1973.

36. On June 26, 1916, in Cleveland, Jack Graney, the first batter up that day for the Cleveland Indians, walked up to the plate with a number pinned on the shoulder of his uniform. Although many fans and sportswriters had suggested this addition to the uniform for many years, the players and owners alike felt that numbering the players was demeaning. In fact this Cleveland innovation didn't last. The numbers were only worn on the sleeve and couldn't be seen from the grandstand. It wasn't until 1929 that numbers were placed in large black numerals on the back of the uniform.

37. Joe DiMaggio, the Yankee Clipper, was the first man to earn that six-figure sum for playing one season of professional baseball for the New York Yankees during the 1950 season.

38. DiMaggio's record during that 1950 season was his worst on record. For the first time in his career he was benched by Casey Stengel, Yankee manager, while batting .275. Yet DiMaggio came back into the lineup at the end of the season with his old strength, slugging the Yanks to a four game sweep of the Philadelphia Whiz Kids and ending his season with an average of .300.

39. The Baltimore Orioles for the Eastern Division and the Minnesota Twins for the Western Division. Baltimore won the contest three games to none.

40. 1931.

41. No, not Jackie Robinson. Moses Fleetwood Walker became the first Black major league ball player when he joined the Toledo club in the Northwestern League in 1883. The Toledo club joined the newly formed American Association in 1884; although the new league wasn't as established as the National League, it was by all means a professional major league. Walker was let go by the Toledo club following a series of threats on his life after he had played 46 games, earning a respectable .251 batting average.

42. It was the great American League impresario Bill Veeck who signed Larry Doby to his Cleveland Indian club in July of 1947. Two weeks later the St. Louis Browns brought up Hank Thompson and Willard Brown.

43. Although Doby was fanned his first time at bat in the seventh inning of a game between the Indians and the White Sox, he began hitting his second game and proved to be an able hitter and fielder. Thompson and Brown didn't fare as well; both were released after only one season. Thompson, however, had a comeback later playing with the New York Giants.

44. The first official baseball World Series was held in 1903 between the Pittsburgh Pirates and the Boston Red Sox, having been prearranged that summer by both teams' owners. The first series was a nine-game affair that lasted a total of thirteen days because of traveling time.

45. Pittsburg pulled off three of the first four games and Boston won the next four to become the first champions of the world, five games to three.

46. Deacon Phillippe pitched a total of 44 innings and won three games during the series for Pittsburgh. Bill Dinneen and Cy Young pitched all the games for Boston.

47. Shibe Park in Philadelphia, built in 1909, is considered to be the first of the modern ball stadiums. The stadium was built of steel and concrete and seated an estimated 20,000 fans. The double-decker grandstand alone had an estimated cost of a half-million dollars.

48. Mickey Mantle was the first player to hit a homer in the Astrodome, during an opening exhibition game between the New York Yankees and the Astros. The Astros won 2-1, before a packed crowd that included President Lyndon Johnson.

49. July 6, 1933, in Chicago.

50. The game was played between the Los Angeles Dodgers and the Houston Astros during a two-game exhibition series on March 19, 1965 in the Astrodome. The surface got mixed reviews from infielders, who claimed that it gave the ball a harder bounce.

51. Mickey Mantle, Stan Musial, Yogi Berra, Joe DiMaggio, Jimmy Foxx, Roy Campanella.

52. The Continental League was used as a threat by those who favored expansion to force the National and American Leagues to add more teams. The league, which was boosted primarily by Branch Rickey, failed before it got started, but it forced the other leagues to expand to ten teams in 1961 and 1962. This was the first change in the size of the leagues in close to sixty years.

53. William A. Hulbert, a memeber of the Chicago Board of Trade and one of the early officers of the Chicago Baseball Club, is credited with founding the National League and in fact saving the game of baseball from disorder and a poor public reputation. Hulbert organized a league of professional clubs all responsible to a major league governing body.

54. The adding of the Montreal franchise to the National League in 1969.

55. The Landis-Eastman Agreement was decided between the commissioner of baseball (Landis) and the head of the Office of Defense Transportation during World War II (Eastman), whereby lines were set up throughout the country south of which professional teams could not travel for spring training. The only exceptions were that the St. Louis Browns and St. Louis Cardinals could train in southern Mississippi. All other teams trained in cold weather spots like Atlantic City, New Jersey, French Link, Indiana, and Medford, Massachusett.

56. To commemorate one hundred years of recorded baseball history the Baseball Hall of Fame was opened in Cooperstown, New York. The first five players inducted into this special society of baseball immortals were Walter Johnson, Christy Mathewson, Ty Cobb, Babe Ruth and Honus Wagner.

57. The Union Association was an early threat to the established National League and fledgling American Association. The Union was first organized on September 12, 1883 and planned to place teams in all major cities.

58. Babe Ruth was chosen the greatest All-Time player by that year's poll; Joe DiMaggio was chosen the greatest living player.

59. The Major League Baseball Player's Association boycotted spring training that year in a dispute with team owners over the pension fund. Almost 150 players boycotted the pre-season games until a settlement was reached with Bowie Kuhn, then the new commissioner of baseball, who agreed to force the owners to add an extra $350,000 annually to the player's pension fund.

60. The following is a list of members, occupations, positions and salaries of that first professional baseball team:

> Fred Waterman, insurance broker, third base $1000
>
> Charles Sweasy, hat maker, second base, $800
>
> Clavin McVey, piano maker, right field, $800
>
> Andy Leonard, hat maker, left field, $800
>
> Charles Gould, bookkeeper, first base, $800
>
> Asa Brainard, insurance broker, pitcher, $1100
>
> George Wright, engraver, shortstop, $1400
>
> Harry Wright, jeweler, center field, $1200
>
> Douglas Allison, marble cutter, catcher, $800

61. The game designed by the Knickerbockers was set to last until either side had scored 21 runs or "aces" during an even number of innings.

62. The Western Association.

63. President Franklin D. Roosevelt requested that both leagues continue functioning even though many of the major stars were drafted. Roosevelt believed that baseball would serve the nation by boosting the morale of the civilian population.

64. Ron Santo, who was then playing for the Chicago Cubs, used the new ruling to restrain his club from trading him to the California Angels.

65. The San Diego Padres, owned by McDonald's president Ray Kroc.

66. Ban Johnson.

67. Cincinnati had permitted liquor and beer to be sold during games, and also permitted then-forbidden Sunday baseball.

68. 1958.

69. Harry Wright, manager of the Cincinnati Red Stockings in 1869.

70. The *New York World,* then run by Joseph Pulitzer, in the 1880s.

71. Altoona, Baltimore, Boston, Chicago, Cincinnati, Kansas City, Milwaukee, Philadelphia, Pittsburgh, St. Louis, St. Paul, Washington, Wilmington.

72. Al Spalding took his Chicago White Stockings on a six-month tour to promote baseball in such exotic places as Australia and Egypt.

73. After setting up the Knickerbockers in New York, Alexander Cartwright headed out west in 1849 in pursuit of a fortune in gold. But Cartwright only stayed a month and headed on a boat to China. He got ill en route and stopped in Hawaii, where he taught the natives the game of baseball. Cartwright lived in Hawaii until his death in 1892.

74. Hal Chase of the New York Highlanders.

75. 1945, because of World War II.

76. In 1901 the American League was founded creating along with the National League the basic structure of major baseball that remains to this day.

77. Bill Klem who umpired in the National League from 1905 until 1940.

78. Joe McGinnity was the pitcher known as the "Iron Man" and he pitched in both the Minor and the Major Leagues for 33 years from 1893 through 1925.

79. Big Ed Walsh.

80. 1969.

81. 1912.

82. 1981.

83. Started June 12; Ended August 9.

Chapter Two

Sluggers, Swingers And Superstars

It was once claimed that Babe Ruth invented the home run. Although a slight exaggeration, few would dispute the claim that it was Ruth who showed the baseball world what the fans wanted to see. They came day after day to see the Bambino reach back and slug the ball into the stands. There had been great hitters before who had dazzled the fancy of many fans. They loved Ty Cobb because of his consistency and wild base running. They loved Nap Lajoie for his flare and showmanship. They loved Wagner and Hornsby because of their daring. But they loved Babe Ruth and the home run the best.

Hitting is the story of the game. If you could draw the origins of baseball as far back as possible, you'd probably wind up back in ancient Egypt where the Pharaohs and their court would bat stones around a field with a flat piece of wood. And today the balls are made to factory and league specifications; the bats have to be a certain weight. But little has changed. No matter how fast a pitcher is, no matter how good his curve or control, it is always the hitter, the power hitter, the place hitter, the doubles, the triples and the home runs that excite the fans.

It was the home run hitting of Ruth that saved the sport of baseball after the decline that followed the 1919 World Series scandal. Something had to be done to salvage the sport from disrepute among the fans. And it was the home run that made them forget. It was the home run battle between Mantle and Maris that stole headlines from presidents, wars and movie stars. It was Ruth, Mays, Mantle, Williams, DiMaggio and Aaron who sold out the box office. And no matter how much Catfish Hunter was paid, no matter how many strikeouts Nolan Ryan throws, it will always be the hitter who will be remembered, the slugger who will win the hearts of the fans.

Sluggers, Swingers and Superstars Quiz

1. What was the rabbit ball and what was its effects?
2. What changes were made to construct a rabbit ball?
3. What effect did the rabbit ball have on the home run hitting of Babe Ruth?
4. What slugger is reported to be the only ballplayer ever to hit a fair ball out of the park at Yankee Stadium?
5. Ty Cobb, Rogers Hornsby and one other slugger hit .400 ball in three seasons, with two of the seasons in a row. Who?
6. Lou Gehrig's brilliant career was put to a sudden halt by what disease?
7. How many games did Gehrig play consecutively?
8. Who was known as the Rajah?
9. What was so unusual about Rogers Hornsby's batting stance?
10. In the 1972 playoffs between the Detroit Tigers and Oakland A's, a batter was suspended for throwing a bat at the pitcher. Who was he?
11. Had anyone been suspended for this before?
12. What home run hitter is said to have been the

only baseball player to have been scouted by his senator?

13. During what World Series did Mickey Mantle break Babe Ruth's after-season home run hitting record? What was the record?

14. Who was Ty Cobb's teammate, who for any other team would have been the celebrated hitting star but for the Tigers was just another player?

15. Who won the American League batting title in 1925?

16. What home run hitter led his league four times for home runs but slugged only 93 in his entire career?

17. How many homers did Hank Aaron finish his career with upon his retirement from baseball?

18. When were Aaron's famed 714th and 715th home runs hit and against what teams?

19. What team was responsible for the perfection of the bunt and hit and run?

20. Who managed that team and what was his other most significant contribution to the sport?

21. What player received the most bases on balls during his career?

22. What trade during the winter of 1926 rocked the entire baseball world?

23. What were Babe Ruth's final hits of his career?

24. Who was the first player inducted into the Hall of Fame before waiting the traditional five-year grace period?

25. How many hits had Roberto Clemente hit by his untimely death?

26. Who was known as the right-handed Babe Ruth?

27. How many homers did Jimmy Foxx finish his career with? If it hadn't been for several bad luck shots, how many would he have hit?

28. Who were the five players who were members of the famed 1932 Yankee Murderer's Row?

29. While Ty Cobb's most memorable lifetime achievement might have been his 2,244 runs, someone has to be credited with driving him in. Who?

30. Eight sluggers in baseball history have batted a season average of .400 or better. Who are they?

31. What was Babe Ruth's record his last year of play?

32. Harmon Killebrew suffered more from the large bonus he was given by the Washington Senators than he benefited. What happened?

33. How did Home Run Baker get his nickname?

34. What hitter was once sued for having hit a home run?

35. Why was Honus Wagner one of the hardest hitters to intentionally walk?

36. In 1966, after an amazing season record of 27 wins and 9 losses, Sandy Koufax was beaten out for his second double crown—MVP and Cy Young Award. Who won the National League MVP that year?

37. What year and from what team did the Yankees acquire Roger Maris? Whom did they trade him for?

38. Lou Gehrig undisputedly holds the record for the most consecutive games played in the American League. Who holds this record for the National League?

39. Who was the last National League player to hit .400 or over in a single season?

40. In 1930 Bill Terry of the Giants won the MVP in the National League. For what?

41. Six hitters in baseball history have won the coveted triple crown award. Who were they and what were their records?

42. What player did even the fearless Ty Cobb claim he couldn't scare?

43. What happened when Ty Cobb and Honus Wagner first met during the 1909 World Series?

44. What was Cobb's average compared to Wagner's during that series?

45. Who won the 1971 American League home run title?

46. When Babe Ruth first broke the American League home run record, whose record did he beat? How many homers did he slug that season?

47. What was Ford Frick's ruling on whether Roger Maris could ever officially beat Babe Ruth's home run record?

48. How did Chuck Klein beat out Mel Ott for the 1929 home run hitting crown?

49. What slugger replaced Bobby Thomson in the outfield for the Milwaukee Braves?

50. In what way was Yankee Stadium built with Babe Ruth in mind?

51. Who's motto was "hit 'em where they ain't"?

52. How did Joe DiMaggio break into professional baseball?

53. While still in the minor leagues, how many games did he hit consecutively in?

54. Whose record did DiMaggio break when he hit in 56 consecutive games?

55. What famed slugger spent half of his career playing with a blinding eye condition?

56. In the season that the M-M boys, Maris and Mantle, raced for Babe Ruth's slugging record of 60 homers, how many homers did Mantle hit?

57. What batter turned down his club's $100,000 contract offer in 1971 because he didn't think he was worth the money?

58. What slugger hailed from Hank Aaron's hometown of Mobile, Alabama?

59. Who said "Hitters who slice singles to the opposite field ride around in jalopies. The hitters who pull the ball into the stands for homers ride around in Cadillacs"?

60. When Ted Williams slugged a batting average of .406 in 1941 he was beaten out for the MVP award. Who won the award that year?

61. What home run hitter was a distant cousin of Babe Ruth?

62. What batter once hit five homers in a single day?

63. Who was the first batter to powder four homers in a single game?

64. Four times in history a batter had led both the American and National Leagues in three categories. Who and when?

65. What batter hit .300 ball twenty out of his twenty-two years in baseball?

66. What batter won his league's batting title the most consecutive years?

67. Who stopped Ty Cobb's streak of batting titles?

68. In 1905 Ty Cobb almost decided not to play professional ball. Why?

69. It is well known that Roger Maris slugged more homers in his 1961 season than Babe Ruth did in 1927; how does the rest of their record for that year compare?

70. Twice during Ralph Kiner's career he threatened Babe Ruth's home run record. When?

71. What batter was traded from the Atlanta Braves to the Boston Red Sox to become the Bosox's first designated hitter?

72. Eddie Stankey once referred to a famed American League slugger as "an all-star ballplayer but only from the neck down." Who?

73. How many batting championships did Rogers Hornsby win during his career?

74. What switch hitting National League slugger hit 25 homers during his rookie year?

75. What Yankee slugger had the nickname of King Kong?

76. What was the team Reggie Jackson hit his 45th homerun off of in 1969 and who was the pitcher?

77. Who stole the most bases in 1982?

78. Who struck out 303 batters in 1978 and was he a right hander or a left hander?

79. What American League player has come to bat the most times in a single season?

Answers

1. The rabbit ball was the new ball introduced in the spring of 1920 to replace the heavier baseball. It was this new ball, livelier and stronger than its predecessor, which revolutionized the sport and ushered in the era of the home run hitter.

2. The rabbit ball was different basically because it was produced from a natural rubber rather than a synthetic rubber. There were also improvements made on the general workmanship of the ball, using better quality horsehide, wool, cement and cotton.

3. In his first season with the New York Yankees, also the first season of the rabbit ball, Babe Ruth socked fifty-four home runs.

4. No, not Babe Ruth. Then who? Josh Gibson, top slugger for the Negro National League, was the only man on record to pound a baseball out of the park that Ruth built. Many claimed back in the 1930s that Gibson was even a greater hitter than the all-mighty Ruth, but unfortunately no official records were kept for the Negro Leagues during Gibson's years as a player. Gibson accomplished this slugging feat in Yankee Stadium in 1934, during a game between his team, the Pittsburgh

Crawfords, and the Philadelphia Stars. It was estimated that Gibson hit as many as 75 homers during the 1931 season while playing for the Homestead Grays.

5. Jesse Burkette slugged .423 in 1895, .410 in 1896 and later hit .402 in 1899. He led the National League during 1895 and 1896, but was surpassed by Ed Delahanty for the 1899 title. Delahanty hit .408 that season.

6. Lou Gehrig was striken by a rare disease known as amytrophic lateral sclerosis, a disease related to infantile paralysis that attacks the central nervous system.

7. It was on May 2, 1939, that Gehrig ended his amazing playing streak of 2,130 consecutive games. Gehrig hadn't been off the field since June 1, 1925.

8. Rogers Hornsby, who during 1924 slugged a walloping .424 that stands as the best season's performance by a batter in either league during modern times. Hornsby ended his career with a .358 batting average.

9. Hornsby's batting style was most unorthodox because he was known to stand as far away from the plate as possible with his feet planted firmly together. He once claimed that it was this stance that allowed him to place the ball wherever he wanted.

10. Nobody knows for sure why he did it, but during the heated playoffs that season Bert Campaneris got so mad at Detroit's pitcher Lerrin Lagrow that he threw his bat at Lagrow's head. Lagrow ducked and missed being hit. Campaneris

was suspended for thirty days in the following season, but the number was eventually reduced to seven.

11. In the last few days of the 1916 pennant race, Ty Cobb flung his bat intentionally at Boston Red Sox hurler Carl Mays, but neither a suspension nor a fine was levied.

12. Harmon Clayton Killebrew not only played for the Washington Senators, but he was originally scouted by one. It was Senator Herman Welker of Idaho who first spotted young Killebrew slugging in his hometown of Payette, Idaho. It was Welker who informed Clark Griffith of the Washington Senators about this budding new talent.

13. It was during the 1964 World Series between the Yankees and the St. Louis Cardinals that Mantle slugged his 16th home run in World Series play, going ahead of Ruth's record of 15. Mantle finished his career with 18 after-season homers.

14. Harry Heilman was a powerful left-handed slugger for the Tigers who never got much attention. Had he not been a switch hitter he probably could have beaten out the Georgia Peach, his colorful and more flamboyant teammate, for many batting titles. Heilman hit .403 in 1923 and came close to reaching that magical mark three other times in his career.

15. Heilman won the batting title that year, slugging .393 and narrowing out Tris Speaker for that year's batting honors.

16. Franklin "Home Run" Baker led the American League four years in a row for home run honors from 1911 until 1914, hitting between eight in 1914 and twelve in 1913. In his 13 years of play, Baker hit only 93 homers, but this was in the days before the rabbit ball, when hitting a home run was a much rarer feat.

17. When Henry Aaron ended his career on September 18, 1976 he had hit 41 home runs more than Babe Ruth's lifetime total, ending his career with 755 home runs.

18. The two most important home runs of Hank Aaron's career were hit when he tied Babe Ruth's home run hitting mark in 1974. At his first time at bat in Cincinnati on April 4, 1974, Aaron slugged his 714th home run off a pitch from the Red's Jack Billingham. His 715th homer was slugged four days later off Dodger hurler Al Downing in the fourth inning of a game in Atlanta Stadium.

19. The Baltimore Orioles of the 1890s, one of the legendary teams in the history of the game, was known for having perfected the inside game of baseball, especially bunts and hit and run plays.

20. Ned Hanlon was the man responsible for that Oriole club during the years of 1890-1894. Possibly his most important contribution to the sport was the institution of spring training in 1894. Other teams scoffed at the practice, but when the team took that year's World Series against the New York Giants four straight, the other teams began "sweating it out" down south, too.

21. Babe Ruth gets this honor with a lifetime total of 2,056 free rides to first.

22. Rogers Hornsby was the idolized player-manager of the St. Louis Cardinals, but just two months after his 1926 victory over the New York

Yankees for that year's World Series, he was traded to the New York Giants for the Fordham Flash —Frankie Frisch. Hornsby and Cardinal owner Sam Breadon had been battling before the trade over Hornsby's demand for a three-year $50,000 salary.

23. The final hits of Babe Ruth's career were home runs number 712, 713 and 714, all hit on May 25. At his final time up at bat Ruth was struck out by Philadelphia pitcher Jim Biven.

24. In 1973 sportswriters unanimously voted to waive the usual five-year waiting period and voted Roberto Clemente, the Pittsburgh Pirate slugger, into the hallowed baseball fraternity. Clemente, who for seventeen seasons slugged, fielded and ran like a Ty Cobb reincarnate, had died in December of 1972 while flying supplies to the victims of an earthquake in Nicaragua.

25. Clemente had just reached that magical plateau of 3,000 hits before his death.

26. Jimmy Foxx, also known as the right-handed Babe Ruth and Double X, once threatened Babe Ruth's home run hitting record by hitting 58 homers during the 1932 season. He twice beat out the Sultan of Swat for MVP nominations.

27. Foxx finished his career with a total of 534 home runs. Had it not been for bad luck Foxx would have slugged four more and would have broken Babe Ruth's home run slugging record of 60 in 1932. During that season Foxx on three occasions hit home runs that happened to strike screens atop fences, thus losing homers and having to settle for ground-rule doubles. On two other occasions the Double X hit homers at the beginning of games that were never finished due to rain, causing his homers to be excluded from the record books.

28. Ruth, Gehrig, Combs, Lazzeri, Dickey.

29. Wahoo Sam Crawford, power hitter for the Detroit Tigers, deserved the credit for having driven the Georgia Peach in for all those runs. Crawford was a home run hitter before the days of the rabbit ball and led his league with homers during the 1908 season with seven.

30. Napoleon Lajoie of the Philadelphia Athletics holds the highest recorded American League batting average with a .422, Shoeless Joe Jackson slugged .408 for the Cleveland Naps in 1911, Ty Cobb came along that year with a .420 for the Detroit Tigers and followed the next year with a .410. The event didn't recur until George Sisler slugged .407 for the St. Louis Browns in 1920. Ty Cobb came back in 1922 to hit .401, Sisler returned in the same year for the Browns, slugging .420, Rogers Hornsby, playing for the St. Louis Cardinals, hit .401 during the 1922 season, and Harry Heilman slugged .403 for the Detroit Tigers in 1923. In 1924 and 1925 Rogers Hornsby held .424 and .403 averages respectively. Bill Terry didn't achieve the feat until 1930, when he hit a .401 for the New York Giants, and finally Ted Williams slugged .406 for the Bosox.

31. Because of illness Ruth only played 28 games during the 1935 season, batting .181.

32. Harmon Killebrew was originally signed to the Washington Senators of a $30,000 bonus. This was the first bonus the Senators had ever paid. But the bonus caused Killebrew more than it was worth. In an attempt to discourage large bonuses to young ballplayers, the league authorities had ruled that players paid a bonus over a certain amount couldn't season out in the minor leagues. As a result Killebrew sat on the bench for his first two seasons, 1954 and 1955.

33. His reputation as well as nickname came when he was playing for Connie Mack's Philadelphia Club in the 1911 World Series. During that series Baker slugged two home runs in two successive games.

34. Sunny Jim Bottomley, slugger for the St. Louis Cards in the 1920s, is most noted for one day hitting in twelve runs against the Brooklyn Dodgers. But he also is noted for being the only hitter ever to be sued for having hit a home run. Bottomley was sued by a fan who was struck by the ball in the grandstand and claimed that Bottomley swung "with the intention of creating a situation known as a homer." Bottomley responded to the charges claiming that "there was never any malice in any of my home runs, just good clean hits."

35. Wagner could hit just about any pitch. He also hated being intentionally passed. In one instance in a game in 1906 against Cincinnati, the pitcher decided it would be better to put Wagner on base than take a chance letting him hit. As is usual with intentional passes, the catcher hopped to the side of the batter's box and the pitcher lobbed the ball out of the reach of the batter. But the Dutchman was not one to stand for simply getting on base. With three balls on him Wagner lunged across the plate for the fourth pitch and sent the ball screaming into the outfield for a double.

36. Although Sandy Koufax easily snagged the Cy Young honors that year he was upstaged for the MVP by Pittsburgh slugger Roberto Clemente.

37. The Yankees traded Hank Bauer, Norm Siebern, Don "Perfect Game" Larsen and Marv Thronberry in 1959 to the Kansas City Athletics in exchange for Joe Demestri, Ken Hadley and Roger Maris.

38. Billy Williams of the Chicago Cubs, with a streak of 1117 games.

39. Bill Terry in 1930, hitting a .401 batting average.

40. Besides his spectacular hitting that year, Terry slugged out 254 safeties in 154 games and played errorless ball at first base for the Giants. Terry finished his career in 1936 with a .341 lifetime batting average, averaging 156 hits per season.

41. 1934—Lou Gehrig (.363, 49 home runs, 167 RBIs)

1937—Joe "Ducky" Medwick (.374, 31 home runs, 154 RBIs)

1942—Ted Williams (.365, 36 home runs, 137 RBIs)

1947—Ted Williams (.343, 32 home runs, 114 RBIs)

1956—Mickey Mantle (.353, 52 home runs, 122 RBIs)

1966—Frank Robinson (.316, 49 home runs, 122 RBIs)

1967—Carl Yastrzemski (.326, 44 home runs, 121 RBIs)

42. Honus Wagner.

43. Honus Wagner and Ty Cobb met only once in their careers, during the 1909 World Series. As the story goes, Cobb had been threatening Wagner throughout game. And when Cobb got on base he yelled down to Wagner, "I'm coming down on the next pitch, krauthead." Wagner just nodded his head. On the next pitch Cobb took off for second. The throw from the catcher was perfect and Wagner easily tagged Cobb out, jamming the ball in his face so that Cobb needed three stitches.

44. Wagner had finished the series with a .333 batting average, stealing six bases. Cobb stole two bases (including home) and batted .231.

45. Going into the final days of the season there was a tie between Reggie Jackson of Oakland, Norm Cash of Detroit, Reggie Smith of the Bosox and Bill Melton of the White Sox, all with 32. Melton broke away from the pack for that year's home run title by slugging a four bagger his second time at bat during that last game of the season.

46. Babe Ruth first set a new home run record in 1919, when he slugged out 29 home runs in a single season. The previous mark was held by Chicago's Ed Williamson, with 27 home runs in 1884. Ruth hit his 29 home runs in a 154-game schedule, while Williamson played a 112-game schedule.

47. When it looked likely that Roger Maris of the New York Yankees would break the immortal

Babe Ruth's home run slugging record, Ford Frick ruled that if Maris were to beat the Babe's record he would have to do it within the 154-game limit. Since it took Maris longer to slug out 61 homers, Frick ruled it would have to be mentioned in all record books that there was a large difference between the two batters' game schedules. Thus Maris could never undisputedly be given the title of home run king.

48. Both Klein and Ott were going neck and neck for that year's title as home run king when both of their teams, the Philadelphia Phillies and the New York Giants, met in a double bill. By the beginning of the second game Klein was one homer ahead of Ott. The Phillies guaranteed that slim lead by walking Ott every time he came up to bat that day, including a fifth walk which brought in a run. Klein won that year's home run crown with 43 homers to Ott's 42.

49. Hank Aaron, then rookie second baseman, was sent into the outfield to replace Thomson. Aaron stayed in the Brave's outfield for twenty years.

50. Yankee owner Jake Ruppert had Yankee Stadium designed and built so that it would be easier for the Babe to slug out homers. Ruppert constructed a right field fence as close as 296 feet, and low enough (43 inches high) so that anything the Babe hit in that direction would get over and into the stands.

51. Wee Willie Keeler, 5' 4", 140 pounds, played for a range of teams, including the Baltimore Orioles and the New York Highlanders, during his career. Keeler was known during his day as the best bunter and place hitter of all time. Keeler, it is said, could pinpoint his hits to within several feet.

52. DiMaggio's big chance came in 1933, when his brother Vince suggested his name to San Francisco Seal's manager Jimmy Caveney as a possible replacement at shortstop. At his first time at bat DiMaggio blasted a triple against Ted Phillete, who was then pitching for the San Francisco Missions.

53. In 1933, his first full season with the San Francisco Seals, DiMaggio hit in 61 consecutive games, from May 28 until July 26.

54. DiMaggio broke Wee Willie Keeler's 44-game record for hitting in consecutive games.

55. George Sisler played fifteen years in the major leagues, accumulated 2,812 hits and finished his career with a .340 batting average, despite the fact that for half those seasons he was threatened with blindness.

56. Mantle ended that season with 54 home runs. The race had been a tight one until the early part of September, when Mantle was struck down with a virus and had to drop out of the contest.

57. Al Kaline, star fielder and slugger for the Detroit Tigers, turned down that six-figure sum. But during that 1971 season Kaline led his club in hitting and accepted the $100,000 for the following season.

58. Willie "Stretch" McCovey, named rookie of the year for his first season with the San Francisco Giants in 1959 by hitting .354 and slugging 13 home runs, was a Mobile hometown favorite.

59. Ralph Kiner was pulling no punches when he admitted that the big money in baseball during his day was to be made by slugging out the home run. Kiner, who was known more for his home run records than for his yearly batting average, made the remark to explain why he was being paid the then-astronomical sum of $90,000 a season for playing for the Pittsburgh Pirates.

60. Although Williams' mark that year was brilliant, it was not quite enough to beat Joe DiMaggio's record of having hit in 56 games during the 1941 season.

61. Stan Musial pulled off that feat by slugging five home runs on May 2, 1954, in a double-header between his St. Louis Cardinals and the New York Giants. Musial hit three home runs in the first game and two in the second. The fifth home run came off Giant pitcher Hoyt Wilhelm, who threw Musial a knuckleball which he clobbered for possibly the longest shot of the day.

63. Bobby Lowe, back in the days when homers were a rarity, hitting four home runs for his Boston Club in 1894. The record was matched the following year by Ed Delehanty of the Philadelphia Phillies.

64. Ty Cobb in 1909, Rogers Hornsby in 1925, Lou Gehrig in 1934, Ted Williams in 1942 and Mickey Mantle in 1956.

65. Adrian "Cap" Anson.

66. Ty Cobb didn't win his first batting title until 1907. At that point he went on to dominate this aspect of the game for the next eight consecutive seasons, until 1916. Cobb further won 12 out of 13 batting titles between the years of 1907 and 1920.

67.   Tris Speaker of the Cleveland Indians broke Cobb's streak in 1916 by hitting .386 compared to Cobb's .371.

68.   Cobb was grieving the death of his father, who had been shot and killed accidentally upon entering his own home, mistaken for a burgler. Cobb contemplated forgetting about baseball but finally reported to the Detroit club on August 30 of that year. Batting fifth in the lineup, Cobb belted out a double at his first time at bat in the major leagues.

69.   In 162 games Roger Maris went to bat officially fifty more times than Babe Ruth did during his 154-game schedule. Maris drew 44 fewer walks, scored 26 fewer runs and made 33 fewer hits. Ruth batted .356 in 1927; Maris slugged .269 in 1961.

70.   Kiner belted 51 homers in 1947 and 52 homers in 1949.

71.   Orlando Cepeda.

72.   Carl Yastrzemski.

73.   Hornsby is credited with seven batting championships during his career.

74.   Eddie Mathews, then of the Boston Braves.

75.   Charlie Keller.

76.   The team was the Baltimore Orioles and the pitcher was Dave McNally.

77.   That was Ricky Henderson of Oakland and he stole 130 bases.

78.   It was the righthanded pitcher, J. R. Richard

Chapter Three

The Men on the Mound

Tris Speaker, famed centerfielder, possibly put it best when he said, "Great pitchers have carried weak hitting teams to a pennant and even a world championship, but no set of hitters and fielders ever carried weak pitchers anywhere out of the second division."

The importance of pitching to any baseball team is without question. A team without a solid starting pitcher and an even more secure bullpen is doomed to the depths of their league. A pitcher without control or without a little something extra on the ball will let the opposition slug anything anywhere. It's the pitching that makes all the difference.

In the early years of the sport the greatest heroes were almost invariably the pitchers. Christy Mathewson, Cy Young, Rube Waddell and other pitching immortals were every fan's idol and every batter's enemy. The rabbit ball, Babe Ruth and the home run had not yet entered the picture and the fans cried for more strike outs, faster pitchers, no-hitters and perfect games.

Then things began to change. The sluggers were paid the bigger salaries. The sports pages devoted endless copy to the power hitters of the day. And the pitchers kept working, losing the fans to the mighty swingers, but becoming no less important to the sport of baseball. Home runs just made better copy and better souvenirs than a fast breaking curve.

Some of the most dramatic players of the history of baseball have been pitchers. Rube Waddell was every bit as colorful as the great Ruth. Cy Young proved more of an Iron Horse than Gehrig. Only in recent years have pitchers once again been given their just regard. Pitchers are again ruling the sport, striking out even the greatest hitters of the day, perfecting their pitches and developing pin-point control. While many fans would cry to relive the moments of the great home run hitters, baseball purists would ask for a perfect game; a Christy Mathewson fadeaway instead of a Babe Ruth home run. Pitching is what the game is all about.

Men on the Mound Quiz

1. Who invented the curve ball?
2. Who first used the curve ball in regular season play?
3. What pitcher is credited with striking out the famed American League Murderer's Row during the All-Star game of 1934?
4. Who were the members of the American League Murderer's Row that year?
5. Who won that year's All-Star game?
6. What was the only double no-hitter in baseball history? Who were the pitchers?
7. Who won the game?
8. What handicapped ballplayer was inducted into the Hall of Fame in Cooperstown, New York?
9. Who was the first major league pitcher to pitch four consecutive shut-outs?
10. Who is the only pitcher to have pitched a perfect game in World Series play?
11. During what game of what World Series was this feat accomplished?
12. What was the final score of that perfect game?
13. Who was the Dodger opposing pitcher during

that famous perfect game and what was his record that day?

14. What was the Feller-Waddell controversy?

15. What was Bob Feller's record during the 1946 season and how did his record compare to Waddell's?

16. What pitcher won more than two hundred games in each major league?

17. What pitcher once replied to a question about how many games he had pitched in his lifetime with "Probably more than you'll ever see in your lifetime"?

18. Who was the first pitcher to have pitched a no-hitter in both leagues?

19. What pitcher put a stop to Joe DiMaggio's famed 56-game hitting streak?

20. What Cincinnati Reds pitcher did the Reds management first hear about while he was pitching in Nuremberg, Germany?

21. In 1965 a fight took place at home plate at Candlestick Park in a game between the San Francisco Giants and Los Angeles Dodgers. It is claimed that this fight cost the Giants that year's title. What happened?

22. What was Carl Hubbell's pitching record during 1933?

23. What change in Don Larsen's pitching style allowed him to become the quality pitcher who could pitch a World Series perfect game?

24. One young American League pitcher never lost a contest he started against the famed Washington Senator hurler Walter Johnson. Who?

25. What pitcher is credited with pitching 56

scoreless innings in a row?

26. What pitcher was noted for having won two World Series games in two days in a row?

27. What was Grover Cleveland Alexander's lifetime strike-out and walk record?

28. Who was the king of the spitball?

29. In 1908 what pitcher worked in 66 games, pitching a total of 464 innings? What was his year's record?

30. What pitcher has accounted for the most no-hitters in a career?

31. Who held the previous record?

32. After Denny McLain's suspension from baseball, to which team did he return in 1971?

33. What was McLain's record during the 1968 season?

34. In 1947 what pitcher won 16 games in a row and finished the season being the best pitcher in the National League in his first full season in the major leagues?

35. The fifth game of the 1955 World Series, possibly the most crucial of that year's series, was won by what young pitcher?

36. In 1971 Charley Finley, owner of the Oakland A's, tried to convince his star hurler Vida Blue to change his name. To what?

37. What pitcher was noted for his famed "fog ball?"

38. What pitcher once struck out Babe Ruth, Lou Gehrig and Bob Meusel in nine straight pitches?

39. What was Lefty Grove's career record?

40. What hurler holds the record for winning the

most double-headers in a career?

41. What great strike-out pitcher never pitched a World Series victory?

42. What hurler broke the record for the most strike outs in a single game but lost the game?

43. Who's record did he break?

44. What was Tom Seaver's record for the 1970 season?

45. In 1906 John McGraw offered $30,000 for a Brooklyn pitcher. Who?

46. What hitter broke up Steve Carlton's famed strike-out performance?

47. What Mets pitcher tied Carlton's record the following season?

48. What pitchers had shared the record for the most consecutive hitters put out on strikes until 1970, when the record was broken?

49. What pitcher led his league in strike outs for seven seasons?

50. What was Iron Man McGinnity's minor league record?

51. What vital call kept Bob Feller from winning a series game during the 1948 World Series?

52. What happened when Dizzy Dean refused to throw any pitch other than his fast ball?

53. Why was Nap Rucker so valuable to the Brooklyn Dodgers during the early part of the twentieth century?

54. Did Nap Rucker ever get a chance to pitch in a World Series game?

55. Who was the oldest rookie ever to play in the major leagues?

56. What pitcher pitched the most shut-out victories in a single World Series?

57. The fourth and winning game for the New York Giants during the 1905 World Series was pitched by whom?

58. In the 1957 World Series a pitcher for the Milwaukee Braves almost matched the record for the most shut-out victories in World Series play. Who?

59. What was his series record?

60. In 1918 the best left-hander in the American League was pulled out of his team's pitching rotation and sent to first base. Why? Who was he?

61. Who did the pitcher replace at first base for the Bosox?

62. What famed left-hander once pitched the ninth inning of a game without any fielders?

63. What famed hurler for the New York Giants had been turned down twice by American League teams before getting his chance in the National League?

64. What team(s) turned him down and why?

65. What was the date Satchel Paige joined the major leagues? What was his first year's record?

66. What was Lew Burdette's record during the 1957 season?

67. What was Babe Ruth's batting record during his first year out of the Boston Red Sox's pitching rotation?

68. What records did Carl Hubbell reach in his 16 years in the majors?

69. Who was the only ballplayer to die as a result of getting hit by a pitch in a major league game?

70. Who was the pitcher?

71. What was so strange about the batter's box score that day?

72. In 1905 Rube Waddell defeated another turn-of-the-century pitching great in what was then billed as "the greatest pitching duel in the history of the game." Who was the other pitcher?

73. What was the result of that game?

74. What was Rube Waddell's best season on record?

75. How did Waddell miss his only opportunity to pitch in a World Series?

76. What pitcher did Dizzy Dean once call "the greatest pitcher who ever lived?"

77. In 1884 a pitcher for the Providence club was pitching a record season, setting numerous pitching marks that still outshadow modern day achievements. Who?

78. Why was pitching much more difficult during the late nineteenth century?

79. When was the first Most Valuable Player award presented and who won?

80. What twist of fate cost Rogers Hornsby that first MVP nomination?

81. In 1959 a pitcher pitched a perfect game and lost. Who?

82. What other time in pitching history did something similar happen?

83. Who was the third Dean brother?

84. How old was Christy Mathewson when he retired from baseball?

85. What two pitching greats share the most

games won during a lifetime in the National League?

86. Although Tom Seaver shattered all types of National League strike-out records during 1970 he lost his chance to win his second Cy Young Award in a row. What National League pitcher won the award that year?

87. In 1968 what pitcher pitched 13 shut-outs and won 15 consecutive games?

88. During the opener of the 1968 World Series what two pitchers started for the two teams?

89. What were the results of that first game?

90. What pitcher once hit two home runs and two doubles in a single game to win his own game, and later that week won three more pitching starts with base hits?

91. Who was the last pitcher to throw a legal spitball?

93. What pitcher led the famed power-hitting 1920s Yankees?

94. What was the name of the Philadelphia Phillies batter who shattered Don Drysdale's 1968 shut-out streak?

95. What record had Drysdale broken at that point and who had held that record previously?

96. What year did Sandy Koufax win both the Cy Young Award and the National League MVP? What was his record that season?

97. In 1963 Sandy Koufax set a World Series record by striking out 15 New York Yankee batters. Whose record did he break and what pitcher did he beat that day?

98. Casey Stengel once sent a pitcher back to the

minors for refusing to dust off a batter. Who?

99. What was Iron Man McGinnity's record during 1903?

100. Why was the 1884 season so difficult for Charlie Radbourne?

101. To whom was this poem by Ring Lardner dedicated?

> My eyes are very misty
> As I pen these lines to Christy
> Oh my heart is full of heaviness today
>
> May the flowers never wither, Matty
> On your grave in Cincinnati
> Which you've chosen for your final fadeaway

102. Off what pitcher did Roger Maris slug his 61st home run?

103. In 1904 the New York Giants had a twenty-game winner who was deaf. Who?

104. What happened when Amos Rusie and Kid Nichols, both late nineteenth-century pitchers, were matched in the pitching duel of that century?

105. Who was the second pitcher to have pitched a no-hitter in both leagues? Who were the last three batters to face him that day?

106. What famous pitcher pitched the most innings in a single session?

107. What famous pitcher pitched the most games in a single season and was he from the American League or the National League?

108. What right-handed pitcher struck out 383 batters, in what year and from what league?

109. Who pitched the last no hitter ever pitched and what team was he playing for?

Answers

1. According to one authority, the curve ball was invented back in 1870, when Fred Goldsmith set up three sticks down the pitching lane to prove that he could make his throw actually curve. Goldsmith tossed the ball down the lane and to the surprise of everyone the ball curved outside the center pole and inside the third. Goldsmith traveled the country showing off his fancy throw, but unfortunately didn't have the control to make the pitch useful in regular season play.

2. Arthur "Candy" Cummings, pitcher for the Brooklyn Stars back in the late nineteenth century, was known for pitching the first curve ball with what he called just a "twist of the wrist."

3. On July 10, 1934, before a crowd of 48,363 at the Polo Grounds in New York, Carl Hubbell, famed hurler for the New York Giants, struck out Murderer's Row.

4. Hubbell had to face the immortal Babe Ruth, Lou Gehrig, Jimmy Foxx, Al Simmons and Joe Cronin. Hubbell struck out Ruth, Gehrig and Foxx in nine pitches in the first inning. He struck out Simmons and Cronin in the second inning in six straight pitches.

5. Despite Hubbell's pitching feat the National League lost the contest to the American, 9-7.

6. On May 2, 1917 baseball history was made when the Chicago Cubs met the Cincinnati Reds for the only double no-hit game in history. Both pitchers, Jim "Hippo" Vaughn of the Cubs and Fred Toney of the Reds, pitched almost perfect ball, both only giving up two bases on balls throughout the entire nine innings of play.

7. The winner was finally decided when in the 10th inning, Vaughn's pitching fell apart and he allowed a single, the first hit of the game. An error allowed the base runner to advance to third, and he was finally sent home with a high bouncing ball to the mound. Toney continued his hitless pitching performance in the bottom half of the 10th inning, striking out the last two hitters to face him.

8. Mordecai Peter Brown, a right-handed pitcher for the Chicago Cubs for 15 years and a member of the championship teams of 1906-1910, was handicapped by the fact that he had only three fingers on his pitching hand. Brown had lost the two fingers while working farm machinery as a boy.

9. Three Finger Brown was the first major league pitcher to pitch four consecutive shut-outs. He ended his career having won 239 games.

10. On October 8, 1957 Don Larsen, New York Yankee hurler, became the first pitcher in the history of the game to throw a perfect game during World Series play.

11. Larsen pulled off the perfect game in the World Series between the Yankees and the

Brooklyn Dodgers during the fifth game of that year's contest. He threw a total of 97 pitches that day, pitching to 27 batters in a row. Thirteen of them popped the ball out, seven grounded the ball out, and seven struck out.

12. Larsen was supported by just enough Yankee hitting, including a Mickey Mantle home run in the fourth inning, to win the game and to bring the Yanks ahead in the series 3-2. Larsen's perfect game was threatened only twice during the game. In the second inning Jackie Robinson slugged a line drive that bounced off of third baseman Andy Carey's mitt, but Gil McDougald saved the day by picking up the ball and quickly throwing Robinson out at first. Sandy Amoros had hit a powerful drive that day but it barely curved foul.

13. Pitching against Larsen was Sal Maglie, who had been favored to be the winning pitcher before gametime that day. Maglie pitched a good game, allowing only five hits.

14. In 1946 it was believed that Bob Feller had beaten Rube Waddell's strike-out record. An investigation by Clifford Kachline, a staff writer for the *Sporting News,* showed that Waddell had actually had more strike outs in the season than had been officially recorded. Feller eventually was given the record because he had pitched ten innings fewer than Waddell had during that year.

15. 1946 was probably Feller's greatest year. He won 26 games, lost 15, pitched 371 innings and finished the year with the record 348 strike outs. Waddell's official record for that mark, set in

1904, had been 343 strike outs, but Kachline had him unofficially fanning 349 batters.

16. Cy Young won a total of 511 games in both the National and American Leagues by the end of his career. 291 games were won in the National League, and 220 in the American League.

17. When asked once by a young reporter how many games he had pitched in his career, Cy Young laughed and replied, "Probably more than you'll ever see in your lifetime." Young wasn't boasting idly, for in his 22 years on the mound, from 1890-1911, he started 906 games, averaging more than 23 wins every season.

18. Cy Young.

19. DiMaggio's streak was stopped during a night game in Cleveland on July 17, 1941 by Indian hurler Al Smith, who walked him once and grounded him out twice. In his last time at bat DiMaggio faced Indian knuckleball pitcher Jim Bagly, who had relieved Smith. On his final time up at bat, in a valiant attempt to salvage his hitting streak, Joltin' Joe smashed a grounder over second base, but the ball took a weird hop and Lou Boudreau was able to get there in time to make a double play.

20. Ewell Blackwell, known as the whip because of his strange but powerful sidearm windup, was first discovered by the Cincinnati club while he was pitching for the 71st Division in Germany. Blackwell won the ETO championship for his team just after VE-Day, winning 16 games, four of which were no-hitters. In his entire army career Blackwell had lost only two games, both 2-1 decisions.

21. The tempers were hot during that game on August 22 between the San Francisco Giants and the Los Angeles Dodgers. When Juan Marichal came up to bat, insults were exchanged with Dodger catcher Johnny Roseboro and soon a fight erupted. Marichal clobbered Roseboro over the head with his bat. The L.A. club converged on the field and a fight broke out. It took at least half an hour for things to settle down. The Giants, who had been pennant contenders, never made it that far, partially because Marichal's pitching wasn't the same again.

22. In 1933 Hubbell, known for his screwball, accumulated a 23-12 record, pitching 10 shut outs, including an 18-inning decision over St. Louis. From July 13 to August 1 of that year, Hubbell pitched 46 consecutive innings of runless ball.

23. Don Larsen's career took a drastic turn for the better when he developed a no-windup delivery. Previously batters could tell whether he was throwing a fastball or a curve by the way he wound up. During that season with the Yanks he had completed only 13 starts, for a 9-2 record. But the change of style late in the season made all the difference.

24. George Herman (Babe) Ruth, then a young southpaw for the Boston Red Sox, beat the famed Walter Johnson every time they met. Ruth faced Johnson for the first time in August of 1915, and went on to beat him the next four times they faced each other. They met each other a total of eight times, but Ruth started only six of these games. Ruth won his six starts against Johnson, three of which were 1-0 narrow wins.

25. Walter "Big Train" Johnson, hurler for the Washington Senators.

26. Grover Cleveland Alexander pulled off this feat well into his career, in 1926. Alexander won the sixth game of the contest and was in the bullpen during the seventh when he was called out by Cardinal manager Rogers Hornsby to pitch. Lou Gehrig was up with bases loaded, threatening the Cards' short 3-2 lead. Alexander struck out the side in the seventh, eighth and ninth innings, giving the Cards the seventh game and their first World Series victory.

27. In his 20-year career Grover Cleveland Alexander walked 953 batters and struck out 2199.

28. The undisputed honors for being king of the spitball goes to Edward A. Walsh, who was the Chicago White Sox's great pitcher.

29. Ed Walsh, often considered one of the greatest pitchers of all time. His final record that season was 40 wins and only 15 losses. The White Sox club that year was so poor that it captured only the league record for the fewest number of home runs hit in a season—three.

30. Sandy Koufax took the title on September 19, 1965, in a game between the Dodgers and the Chicago Cubs. Koufax pitched his fourth no-hitter, in fact a perfect game, against the Cubs. The Dodgers won the contest 1-0.

31. The previous record for the most no-hitters

in a career was jointly held by Cy Young and Bob Feller, who both had pitched three.

32. Upon his return to professional baseball, McLain first pitched for Ted Williams' Texas Rangers; he lost 22 games out of the 32 he started. McLain never seemed to get back his rhythm and was eventually traded to Charley Finley's Oakland club, where he won only one game and lost two, finishing the season with an ERA of six. He was traded the following season to the Atlanta Braves, and was eventually released in 1973.

33. McLain won 31 games and lost 6 during the 1968 season.

34. During his first full season with the Reds, 1947, Ewell Blackwell won 22 games. Sixteen of these wins were in a row.

35. Roger Craig's biggest moment came in the fifth game of the 1955 World Series, between the New York Yankees and his team, the Brooklyn Dodgers. Although he only pitched six innings, he allowed just three hits by the power-hitting Yankee club. With his performance and Duke Snider's two homers that day, the Brooklyn Dodgers went ahead and later became World Series champs.

36. To boost attendance and please the fans Finley tried to convince Vida Blue to change his real name to "True." He had offered Blue a bonus for going along with the publicity stunt but Blue refused, feeling that it would be demeaning.

37. No other pitcher but the colorful Dizzy Dean could claim such a pitch. This was Dean's pet name for his famed fastball. When once asked how he threw a ball, Dean declared, "I just rear back and fog 'em down the alley."

38. Robert Moses "Lefty" Grove once struck out these three Yankee power hitters with nine straight pitches, while pitching for Connie Mack's Philadelphia Athletics.

39. Grove's career record shows an average win of 25 games per season. In 1930 he appeared in as many as 50 games, winning 28. His record still improved and in 1931 he won 31 games, losing only 4, a total winning average of .886 for that season. It was during that season that Grove won 16 straight games.

40. Iron Man Joe McGinnity, pitchingmate of the immortal Christy Mathewson of the New York Giants, is best remembered for his record of having won three twin bills in a single season. In fact, McGinnity pitched all three of these double-headers in a single month, August of 1903, McGinnity's best season. McGinnity won all six games. In one of the games he allowed only one run, in two others he allowed two runs and in the third he allowed three runs. In fact, McGinnity won one of these contests himself when, in the latter portion of the game, he stole home with the winning run.

41. Bob Feller, who thoughout his 21 years in the major leagues shattered every existing strike-out record, never won a World Series game. During his one possible chance in the 1948 World Series, Feller pitched a brilliant three hitter but still lost against the Boston Brave's Johnny Sain in a 1-0 decision.

42. This dubious distinction must go to Steve Carlton, southpaw for the St. Louis Cardinals, who on September 15, 1969, pulled off the impossible by striking out 19 batters but still losing the game.

43. Carlton broke the record that had been held jointly by Sandy Koufax, Bob Feller and Don Wilson.

44. Seaver won 18 games and lost 12, striking out ten batters a game for twelve games and leading the league that year with 283 strike outs.

45. Back in the early part of the twentieth century George "Nap" Rucker was considered with such pitching immortals as Christy Mathewson and Walter Johnson. McGraw's $30,000 offer, one of the highest at the time, was immediately turned down by Dodger owner Charlie Ebbets.

46. Ron Swoboda, New York Mets power hitter, blasted two home runs that day, making the difference. The Mets won the game despite Carlton's record, 4-3.

47. Tom Seaver matched that record on April 22, 1970, in a contest between the Mets and the San Diego Padres. During that game Seaver put down 19 batters, including the last ten batters to face him that day.

48. Seaver broke a record for most consecutive strike outs shared by Max Surkont, Johnny Podres, Jim Mahoney and Don Wilson, all of whom had struck out eight batters.

49. Bob Feller, who during his career struck out 2,581 batters. It has been said that if Feller hadn't missed four crucial years at the height of his career because of the war he would surely have surpassed the magic 300-game winning mark and would have added an extra 1,000 strike outs to his career total.

50. After leaving the Giants, Iron Man Joe McGinnity went on to pitch 204 games in the minor leagues. In his first season with the Newark club he won 59 games; continued in the minors until he was 54, when he pitched a 6-6 season for the Dubuque club in 1925.

51. It is said that Bob Feller would have had his one chance to win a World Series game if it hadn't been for a bad call by the umpire. During that game a perfectly executed pick-off play between the catcher and shortstop Lou Boudreau caught the Boston runner, Phil Masi, off guard and he was obviously tagged out. But the umpire wasn't paying attention and called Masi safe. Masi eventually scored with the only run of the day.

52. In a game against Boston, Dizzy Dean once announced boldly that he wouldn't pitch a curve ball all day. And he didn't. He just kept throwing his famed fast or "fog" ball over the plate and struck out numerous Boston hitters. He shut out the Boston club that day and allowed only three hits, winning the game by a final score of 3-0.

53. Rucker worked over 40 games a season for the Brooklyn club, but because he had a poor hitting team behind him he won no more than 18 games a season. He did, however, account for one of the games' first recorded no-hitters, in 1908.

54. Rucker didn't have a chance to play in a World Series game until the last year of his career, by which time he was suffering from bursitis in his pitching hand and had won only two games all year. Rucker pitched two innings for the Brooklyn club and struck out three batters, allowing no runs.

55. Satchel Paige, with the official age of 42. Others claim he was older, with his birthday actually being in 1899.

56. Christy Mathewson, or the Big Six as he was known, threw three shut outs during the 1905 World Series contest between the Giants and Connie Mack's Philadelphia Athletics. Mathewson shut out the American League champions 3-0, 9-0 and 2-0, allowing as few as four hits in the first two appearances and six hits in the third.

57. The fourth and winning game for the Giants that year was pitched by Iron Man McGinnity, who also pitched a shut out.

58. Lew Burdette led the Milwaukee Braves in three individual victories over the power-hitting Yankees in the 1957 World Series.

59. Burdette defeated the world champion Yankees, 1-0, 5-0, and 4-2, allowing only two runs in 27 innings of World Series play.

60. Babe Ruth was too valuable a home run hitter for the Bosox to waste in the pitching rotation.

61. Ruth replaced Dick Hoblitzell, the Bosox first baseman and clean-up hitter who was in a lengthy slump. Hoblitzell had injured his hand slightly and the team manager took the opportunity to pull Hoblitzell out of the lineup and plug Ruth in at first base.

62. George ''Rube'' Waddell, one of the zaniest players in the history of the game, pulled this stunt while playing an exhibition game against the Memphis team. The Athletics were ahead 6-0. Waddell called his fielders off the field in the bottom of the ninth inning and proceeded to strike out the first two batters. In fact, he even struck out the third batter but his catcher, Mike Powers, dropped the ball on the third strike and the batter got on base. The Memphis team followed up with two base hits, putting three men on base. Waddell then threw three straight strikes and whiffed the final batter, allowing no runs.

63. Carl Hubbell.

64. Originally Hubbell had been brought into the majors by the Detroit Tigers. Tiger manager Ty Cobb believed that Hubbell's strange pitching style would force him into an early retirement. Hubbell was turned down two years later by manager George Moriarity, who, like Cobb, believed that Hubbell's screwball pitch wouldn't last long against some of the hitting greats of the day.

65. Paige joined the Cleveland Indians on July 9, 1948, and ended his first year in the major leagues with a 6-1 record.

66. Burdette's record during that season had been the best in his career, with 17 wins and 9 losses. Burdette was reputed to be one of the most flagrant violators of the game's spitball rule.

67. By May 6, 1918, Babe Ruth was officially given the sixth batting slot for the Boston Red Sox. On that eventful day Ruth slugged his second homer in two days. When the next game came up in Washington, D.C., Ruth was moved up to the clean-up slot and again he hit a home run. His batting average quickly rose to .348. He finished the season with a .300 batting average, slugging 11 home runs.

68. In his sixteen seasons with the Giants, Hubbell pitched 46½ innings without allowing a single run, and won 24 games in a row between the 1935 and 1936 seasons.

69. Ray Chapman, a brilliant Cleveland Indian shortstop.

70. Chapman was struck on the head by a pitch thrown by Boston Red Sox hurler Carl Mays, a noted submarine-ball pitcher.

71. On that day Chapman, for some mysterious reason, had been doing everything in "twos." He was batting number two in the Indian lineup, he had stolen two bases and come in with two runs. In the field that day he had made two errors, put out two runners and been struck by two pitches, including the fatal one.

72. Cy Young, then 38 years old and pitching for the Boston Red Sox, on July 4, 1905, in Philadelphia.

73. The two pitching immortals battled for a total of 20 innings before the game was decided. In the twentieth inning a Red Sox error gave up two runs, giving the Athletics the edge and the victory. Young didn't walk a batter all day but lost the game, 4-2.

74. That 1905 season was Waddell's best on record. He won 24 games and lost 11, with an ERA of 1.48 and 287 strike outs, even though he missed the final five weeks as a result of an injury.

75. Waddell loved horseplay and was hurt when his teammate Andy Coakley struck him on the arm with a suitcase. Waddell slipped and fell, badly bruising his right shoulder. Waddell missed the final five weeks of the season and his only World Series chance as a result of the accident.

76. Had Satchel Paige been pitching in the big leagues at the height of his career, there is no telling how great he could have been. Many who had seen him play in the Negro National League, including Dizzy Dean, claimed he was the best pitcher who ever lived.

77. 1884 was a magical season for oldtimer Charles "Hoss" Radbourne, who compiled an amazing record of pitching 75 games and finishing the season with a 60-12 record. Radbourne is reported to have struck out 441 batters that year. During his ten-year career Radbourne pitched in 528 games, winning 308.

78. In the early days of the game the batter was at a distinct advantage. He could swing any size club he could lift. The pitcher stood only 50 feet away from the plate, giving most pitches no time to break. The batter could also demand either a high or low pitch.

79. This annual presentation was started in 1924, the same year that Rogers Hornsby racked up his record .424 batting average for the Cardinals. But Hornsby was beaten out for the first MVP by Brooklyn pitcher Dazzy Vance, who had finished the season with an impressive 28-6 record.

80. An investigation into the balloting of the first MVP revealed that the only reason Vance beat out Hornsby for the distinction was that a Cincinnati columnist omitted Hornsby from the list altogether. All other lists had Hornsby at the top spot.

81. On May 26, 1959, Harvey Haddix pitched 12 innings of perfect ball against the Milwaukee Braves and lost the game and his pitching streak in the 13th. Haddix, pitching for the Pittsburgh Pirates, retired the first 36 batters to face him, a major league record.

82. A similar occurrence happened in 1906, when Harry McIntire of the Brooklyn Dodgers pitched 10 2/3 innings of perfect ball in a game against Pittsburgh but lost the contest in the 13th inning by a score of 1-0.

83. There was Dizzy and Paul and who else? Nobody even knew there was a third Dean brother back in the days that the dynamic duo were burning up the National League. It was Casey Stengel who first demanded to know the whereabouts of the third brother, Elmer, who was rumored to have been playing somewhere in Houston. But Stengel and the rest of the major leagues soon learned that the third Dean brother's only connection with the sport of baseball was that he sold peanuts at the Houston ballgames in the Texas League.

84. Christy Mathewson was 39 years old and suffering from tuberculosis when he retired from active playing. He returned to the sport in an administrative position in 1932 to take over the Boston Braves as team president.

85. Christy Mathewson and Grove Cleveland

Alexander both share the National League record for most games won, 373.

86. Bob Gibson, hurler for the St. Louis Cardinals, won the 1970 Cy Young Award, having fanned over 200 batters for the eighth time in his career. Previous holders of this mark had been pitching immortals Rube Waddell and Walter Johnson. The right-handed Gibson also compiled an impressive 23-7 season's record during 1970.

87. Bob Gibson who also won the Cy Young Award during that season.

88. Bob Gibson for the St. Louis Cardinals and Denny McLain for the Detroit Tigers.

89. Gibson fanned 17 Tigers that day, beating the Tigers' 31-game winning hurler, McLain, in a 4-0 decision.

90. In 1890 Kid Nichols, who goes down in the record books as having won over 30 games per season for seven seasons with the Boston club, was for a time one of the best hitters in the league and accomplished this feat. Playing for Frank Selee's Boston Beaneaters, Nichols pitched a total of 12 seasons, winning at least 20 games every year of his career.

91. Burleigh Grimes threw the last legal spitball at the end of the 1934 season. Grimes had probably the best control of any spitballer and was also known for a lively fastball curve.

92. The spitball had been ruled illegal as far back as 1920, but there was an added provision in 1921 that allowed eight National League and nine American League pitchers to use the pitch for the rest of their careers.

93. Herbert J. Pennock collected five World Series victories, including two masterful three-hitters while pitching for the Yanks. He was most noted for his victory during the 1927 World Series between the Yankees and the Pittsburgh Pirates, where he blanked the first 22 Pirates to come up against him during the third game of that year's championship series.

94. A Philadelphia Phillies pinch hitter, Howie Bedell, ruined Don Drysdale's streak on June 8, 1968, in the fifth inning at Chavez Ravine. Bedell tagged a fly ball to left field, driving in Phillies runner Tony Taylor. Bedell had only been up seven times before that season.

95. Drysdale had shattered the 50-year-old record held by Washington Senators immortal Walter Johnson. Johnson had pitched 56 scoreless innings in 1913. When Drysdale met Bedell he had already beaten that mark, having pitched 58 2/3 shut-out innings.

96. In 1963 Sandy Koufax both won the MVP and the Cy Young Award, pitching a brilliant 25-5 record that season, including an amazing no-hit performance against the Giants in which he walked only two batters.

97. Koufax set a World Series record by striking out 15 New York Yankee batters, breaking Carl Erskine's record and beating Whitey Ford and the Yankees in his first World Series win, 5-2.

98. As Stengel tells the story, he instructed a young left-hander named Warren Spahn to dust off a pitcher. Spahn refused and Stengel sent him back to the minors, claiming "you've got no guts."

Two years later Spahn had won 21 games and lost 10. He finished his career with 363 wins.

99. McGinnity pitched 434 innings that year, faced 1658 batters and finished the season winning 31 games.

100. During the 1884 season Providence had no other pitching to rely on. The other Providence star hurler, Charlie Sweeney, was out for the season due to injuries. Sweeney had set a National League strike-out record by fanning 19 Boston hitters, but never finished the season. Radbourne was saddled with the responsibility of pitching the team to the championship. During that season he achieved his total of 60 wins.

101. Christy Mathewson, who was noted for his famed fadeaway pitch.

102. The record blast came off a pitch by Tracy Stallard, then of the Boston Red Sox.

103. Luther "Dummy" Taylor was the only deaf-mute to play professional baseball. His biggest season was in 1904, the year John McGraw refused to play the World Series, when he won 21 games. For ten more years he pitched in the major leagues, finishing his career with a total of 116 wins.

104. For 13 innings they battled. Nichols allowed only four hits and put away ten men on strike outs. Rusie did slightly better, giving up only three hits and striking out eleven men. Rusie eventually won the contest on a game-winning home run by Mike Tiernan, the New York Giant centerfielder.

105. Jim Bunning, then pitching for the Philadelphia Phillies, became the second pitcher in the history of the game to have pitched a no-hit game in both leagues when he pitched against the New York Mets on June 21, 1964. To top it off, he pitched a perfect game that day. Bunning was the first pitcher to pitch a perfect game in regular season play in over 42 years. The last three batters to face him that day were: Charlie Smith (popped out to Cookie Rojas), George Altman (struck out), and John Stephenson (struck out).

106. In 1908 Edward Walsh of Chicago pitched 464 innings.

107. In 1974 Mike Marshall from Los Angeles and the National League pitched 106 games in a single session.

108. In 1973 Nolan Ryan of California struck out 383 batters in a single season while playing in the American League.

109. On May 15, 1981 Len Barker playing for Cleveland pitched a no hitter. It was only the 12th no hitter in baseball history.

Chapter Four

Runners, Fielders and Other Strangers

The game of baseball is not entirely devoted to pitching and slugging. There have to be players who can chase down a hard grounder, chase after a line drive, dive, jump, catch, run and add a further dimension to the sport. There are nine players in every lineup and nine players on every field. And although the history of the game has been dominated by those who could swing harder and those who could pitch faster than the rest, it would be foolish to ignore the remaining players, who have often played their hearts out over the years for little or no permanent recognition. While the MVP, the home run title, the Cy Young Award, and the strike-out title receive headlines each year in the papers, the Golden Glove Award and the most stolen bases record are often ignored. A good glovesman is as important to a good team as a good hitter and good pitcher. A man who can steal bases gives a good team the extra edge to become a great team.

And what about the others—the umpires, the bat boys and the rest that have contributed to making the game what it is today? There are too many to list, too many trivia questions to be asked about this vast range of players and baseball notaries. Many of them have crossed over into other chapters. Many great fielders and runners were also great hitters, many made their mark in World Series competition and many became managers or were members of great teams. These have and will be covered in other chapters. But as a tribute to those who have often been ignored next to the slugging and pitching superstars, you will find a sampling of other baseball luminaries who have contributed much to the greatness of our national pastime.

Runners, Fielders and Other Strangers Quiz

1. What second baseman set the record for the most consecutive games without an error, then broke his own record one year later?

2. Who is known for his famed $40,000 assist?

3. What player was credited with the perfection of the slide?

4. What were the words to the song "Slide, Kelly, Slide?"

5. Who was the first base runner ever to slide?

6. If it hadn't been for a slight misunderstanding, what Black ballplayer would have broken the major league color barrier instead of Jackie Robinson?

7. What year did that ballplayer first play in the major leagues?

8. Who were the players in Connie Mack's $100,000 infield?

9. In what game did Phil Rizzuto make his famed barehanded, backhanded catch?

10. Off what batter was that ball hit?

11. Who was the most famous batboy in the history of the game?

12. Who replaced Ray Chapman at shortstop for the Cleveland Indians?

13. In the 1970 World Series, what fielder was awarded the MVP award for the World Series by *Sport* magazine?

14. What was his record during that series?

15. What Brooklyn Dodger catcher won the MVP three times?

16. In 1901 John McGraw, then manager of the Baltimore Orioles, tried to get a Black second baseman to play for his team. Who?

17. What fielder and batter holds the dubious honor of being hit by the most pitches in a single day?

18. When Lou Brock broke Maury Wills' base-stealing record in 1974, how many bases did he steal?

19. Who's record did Wills break when he made his mark in 1962?

20. What Boston Red Sox catcher risked his life on numerous occasions as an American spy during World War II?

21. What Detroit Tiger second baseman once came up to bat wearing a raincoat and carrying an umbrella? Why?

22. What centerfielder was once a professional stuntman?

23. Name the outfielders for the 1939 Brooklyn Dodgers.

24. What second baseman holds the record for the most double plays in a career?

25. What two brothers were famed outfielders for the 1925 Pittsburgh Pirates?

26. Name the 1960 New York Yankee infield.

27. What catcher is the lifetime double-play

leader?

28. What first baseman played the most lifetime games?

29. Who is responsible for the practice of infielders backing each other up on plays?

30. Who were the Wright Brothers of baseball?

31. Who was the first catcher to wear shin guards?

32. What shortstop is credited with the most lifetime double plays?

33. What are the saddest of all possible words?

34. What rightfielder is credited with giving the Boston club the four national championships between 1872 and 1875?

35. Who was Bill Klem?

36. How many games did he judge in his career?

37. What outfielder holds the best fielding average for a single season?

38. What umpires are in the Hall of Fame?

39. What happened during the famous confrontation between Bill Klem and John McGraw?

40. What catcher once hit a home run in total darkness?

41. Early in his career Willie Mays pulled off one of the most amazing double plays in the history of fielding. What happened?

42. Who was the batter?

43. What shortstop was noted for his unusual way of catching fly balls?

44. Who holds the record for the most put-outs at first base by a first baseman in a single game?

45. Match each of the following fielding positions with the players below: catcher, outfield, third base, second base, shortstop, first base.

1. Willie McCovey
2. Rogers Hornsby
3. Johnny Roseboro
4. Eddie Yost
5. Ron Swoboda
6. Ron Hunt
7. Ed Delahanty
8. Boog Powell
9. Pee Wee Reese
10. Choo Choo Coleman

46. Name the infielders for the New York Yankees and the Brooklyn Dodgers during the 1953 World Series.

47. Name the outfielders for the Oakland Athletics and the Detroit Tigers during the 1971 American League playoffs.

48. Name the catchers for the Los Angeles Dodgers and the New York Yankees during the 1963 World Series.

49. Joe Rudi of the Oakland A's possibly made the greatest catch in the history of the game during the 1972 World Series. Who hit the ball?

50. Who is often referred to as the "last of the left-handed third basemen?"

51. Who was Willie Randolph and what team was he famous for playing with?

52. Who was a famous slugger, a fantastic outfielder and one of the best outfielders on the Yankees team in 1978?

53. What famous Yankee catcher was killed in a plane crash in 1979?

Answers

1. Albert Fred "Red" Schoendienst, the great second baseman for the St. Louis Cardinals, New York Giants and Boston Braves, made his first record when he played 44 games and handled 285 balls without an error in 1949. His stretch lasted from September 1948 until May 1949. He later broke his own National League mark when in 1950 he handled 320 balls in 67 games between the end of May and the end of July without an error.

2. Schoendienst will be remembered most for his famed $40,000 assist during the 1946 World Series between the St. Louis Cardinals and the Boston Red Sox. Schoendienst had pulled off 21 assists during that seven-game series, the last of which, during the seventh game, made the difference between the winner's and loser's share of the prize money—$40,000.

3. Mike "King" Kelly, who played for the then unbeatable Chicago White Stockings, was noted for his innovation of the hook slide. In 1873 Kelly began experimenting with different variations on the slide. His reputation as a base runner became widespread after he had perfected what became known as the Chicago slide, an early version of the hook slide.

4. Slide, Kelly, slide
    Your running's a disgrace
    Slide, Kelly, slide
    Stay there hold your base

    If someone doesn't steal you
    And your batting doesn't fail you
    They'll take you to Australia
    Slide, Kelly, slide

5. Eddie Cuthbert, in the early 1860s.

6. Roy Campanella was the first Black ballplayer offered a contract with Branch Rickey's Brooklyn Dodgers. But when the future Brooklyn catcher heard the offer he thought it was for another Negro League team and declined.

7. Campanella finally broke into the major leagues with the Brooklyn Dodgers in 1948, first reporting to the Brooklyn team's Class B club in New Hampshire.

8. Eddie Collins at second base, Jack Berry at shortstop, Stuffy McInnis at first base, and Home Run Baker at third base.

9. In the second inning of the September 23, 1951 game between the Cleveland Indians and New York Yankees, Yankee shortstop Phil Rizzuto pulled a short leftfield hit out of nowhere with his bare right hand, snagging the ball just 20 feet inside the foul line.

10. Jim Hegan.

11. Eddie Bennett, a hunchback, whom many players believed to be good luck. Some believed

that a team could get good luck simply by rubbing his back. Bennett's services made him the highest paid batboy in the history of the game, and the clubs often bidded for his services. All three teams that Bennett worked for—the Chicago White Sox, the Brooklyn Dodgers, and the New York Yankees —were pennant winners.

12. It was Chapman's death that brought University of Alabama shortstop Joey Sewell off the bench and into the game of baseball for the next 20 years.

13. Brooks Robinson, famed hot-corner specialist for the Baltimore Orioles, was given that special honor. In addition, his performance during that series was so spectacular that it was requested that his glove be donated to the Baseball Hall of Fame in Cooperstown, New York.

14. Robinson exploded in every aspect of the game, collecting nine hits in 21 times at bat and ending the series with a .429 batting average. In the field he stopped almost anything that came his way, making every play that was humanly possible.

15. Roy Campanella.

16. A Cincinnati second baseman named Charlie Grant might have beaten Jackie Robinson out by as many as 46 years if John McGraw had been able to convince the baseball world that Grant, a Black man, was actually an Indian named Charlie Tokohoma. But the deal was called off because of racism, and Grant went instead to play for the Columbian Giants.

17. During a doubleheader on May 30, 1904,

Frank Chance of the Chicago Cubs was hit by the opposing pitchers three times during the first game and by two more pitches in the second half of the twin bill for a total of five free rides to first and five free bruises.

18. Brock broke Maury Wills' 12-year old record of 104 stolen bases in one season by snagging 118 bags that year, making it the eighth year he led the league in stolen bases and the tenth year in a row he had stolen more than 50 bags in a single season.

19. Back in 1962, when Maury Wills, the young L.A. shortstop, was tearing up the baseline, he was breaking the 47-year-old record held by Detroit Tiger great Ty Cobb. Cobb had stolen 96 bases in his 154-game season in 1915.

20. Moe Berg, who during his baseball career caught for the Chicago White Sox and the Boston Red Sox, was among other things a scholar and an atomic spy for the United States. Berg ended his baseball career with a batting average of .259. He spent World War II spying on Nazi nuclear energy and weaponry projects.

21. The Detroit Tigers and Cleveland Indians were playing in heavy rain, and umpire Tommy Connolly refused to call the contest until Germany Schaefer, second baseman for the Tigers, came out to bat dressed in hip boots, a raincoat and carrying an umbrella. Connolly eventually called the game after Schaefer refused to remove his attire.

22. Ernie Orsatti, centerfielder for the 1934 Gas House Gang, was nicknamed ''Showboat'' not only for the stunts he pulled in the outfield, but because he spent his off season acting as a stuntman in Hollywood, including doubling for comedian Buster Keaton.

23. Gene Moore, Art Parks, Dixie Walker, Goody Rosen, Mel Almada, Ernie Koy, Jimmy Ripple and Fred Sington.

24. Bill Mazeroski (1706).

25. Paul (Big Poison) and Lloyd (Little Poison) Waner.

26. Clete Boyer (third base), Tony Kubek (short), Bobby Richardson (second base) and Bill Skowran (first base).

27. Ray Schalk, with a career total of 221.

28. Not Lou Gehrig. Jake Beckley, with a total of 2,377.

29. Charlie Cominsky, then player-manager of the St. Louis Browns, started this practice. Cominsky was also responsible for other fielding innovations, like having the first baseman play behind the bag and having the pitcher run to first whenever the first baseman had to play the ball.

30. Harry, George and Sam Wright were possibly the game of baseball's first superstars, playing in the early years just after the Civil War. It was George who later became the greatest of the three. All of them had gotten their early training playing cricket in England.

31. Roger Bresnahan of the New York Giants was the first catcher to wear shin guards.

32. Luis Aparicio, with 1533.

33. Tinker to Evers to Chance. This was the first stanza from a poem written by Franklin P. Adams about the famed Chicago Cubs double-play com-

bination. It goes,

> These are the saddest of all possible words
> > Tinker to Evers to Chance
>
> Trio of bear Cubs and fleeter than birds
> > Tinker to Evers to Chance
>
> Ruthlessly pricking our gonfalon bubble
> making a Giant hit into a double
> Words that are weighty with nothing but
> trouble
> > Tinker to Evers to Chance

34. George Wright.

35. William J. Klem, also known as the Old Arbitrator, was probably the most famous umpire in the history of the game. After he retired he boldly claimed, "I never called one wrong."

36. Klem judged a total of 5,000 games and 18 World Series games in his 36-year career.

37. Curt Flood, who never made an error despite 396 opportunities during the 1966 season, for a 1.000 fielding average.

38. Jocko Conolan, Thomas Connolly, William G. Evans, William J. Klem, Carl Hubbard.

39. During a contest on April 25, 1913 between the New York Giants and the Philadelphia Phillies, Klem demanded that a game-winning single for the Giants be cancelled because he had had his back turned when the pitch was thrown. He instructed the pitcher to throw another pitch, and this time the Giant batter grounded out. Giant manager John McGraw rushed out on the field screaming, "I'll have your job for this."

Klem calmly replied, "If that were possible Mr. McGraw, I wouldn't want it any more."

40. Charles "Gabby" Hartnett, catcher for the Chicago Cubs from 1926 to 1939, hit this clutch homer during the 1938 season. It was the last game of the season and the Cubs needed one win to go ahead of the Pirates for the pennant. In the bottom of the ninth, two outs and darkness closing in fast, Hartnett stepped up to bat against Pirate hurler, Big Mace Brown. Mace got two strikes on Hartnett and threw a fast breaking curve while the Cub catcher socked over the leftfield fence. It was so dark that it took a ruling from all the umpires to make sure it had been hit fair.

41. Mays, still a rookie, caught a hard and long drive to centerfield in the bottom of the eighth inning. Billy Cox, the lead runner on third, headed for home but Mays whirled around and rocketed the ball to home to catch Cox out.

42. Carl Furillo.

43. Walter "Rabbit" Maranville was noted for his unusual way of catching the ball. He would first let it strike his chest and then let it roll down to his waist and into his mitt.

44. The mark was originally set by famed first baseman Hal Chase, who made 22 put outs during a single game. The mark was later tied by Tom Jones of the St. Louis Browns. Later in his career Chase made 38 put outs at first base during a doubleheader.

45.   1.   Willie McCovey—first base
        2.   Rogers Hornsby—second base
        3.   Johnny Roseboro—catcher
        4.   Eddie Yost—third base
        5.   Ron Swoboda—outfield

6. Ron Hunt—second base
7. Ed Delahanty—outfield
8. Boog Powell—first base
9. Pee Wee Reese—shortstop
10. Choo Choo Coleman—catcher

46. New York Yankees
1b Joe Collins
2b Billy Martin
3b Gil McDougald
ss Phil Rizzuto

Brooklyn Dodgers
1b Gil Hodges
2b Junior Gilliam
3b Billy Cox
ss Pee Wee Reese

47. Oakland Atheltics
Joe Rudi
Reggie Jackson
Matty Alou

Detroit Tigers
Al Kaline
Jim Northrup
Willie Horton

48. Los Angeles Dodgers
Johnny Roseboro

New York Yankees
Elston Howard

49. Denis Menke of the Cincinnati Reds.

50. Willie Keeler, who spent the later years of his career in the outfield.

51. Willie Randolph was the Yankees second baseman in 1978.

52. Reggie Jackson.

53. Thurman Munson.

Chapter Five

Great Managers and Great Teams

Casey Stengel was once asked why he didn't have any great teams until he became manager of the New York Yankees. Stengel, who had managed the Dodgers and the Braves for ten years without pulling either club out of the second division, looked perplexed, then replied, " 'Cause I never had any great players, that's why."

Stengel was indeed one of the greatest managers in the history of the game, leading his New York Yankees from 1949 to 14 pennants in the next 16 years, but he was aware, as are all managers, that even the most brilliant tactician, the most skilled trainer and scout cannot do anything with a talentless ball club. Leo Durocher, a managerial genius despite his loud and often obnoxious ways, was saddled with a poor Brooklyn club for many years and only won three National League pennants. Had he had a team and back-up organization of the caliber of Stengel's Yankees, there is no telling what could have happened.

And what about those teams? A good team doesn't just happen by accident. It takes years of good scouting. It takes a well-founded farm system to prune out the good from the bad and to train the good to be better. It takes money, especially today. And of course it takes luck, a good late-inning call, a future Babe Ruth or Bob Feller who happens to walk into spring training one day, a pinch hitter who blasts the ball out of the stadium with two out and bases loaded. These are the ingredients of a winning ball club. And it is when a winning ball club is coupled with a talented manager that things start to happen, when the sport is taken to its extremes.

Great Managers and Great Teams Quiz

1. In 1966 in New York the Yankees were in last place and the Mets weren't. How did the Mets finish that year?
2. What year did Mets manager Casey Stengel retire from baseball?
3. Who replaced Stengel?
4. What baseball manager penned the famous Baseball Ten Commandments?
5. What were they?
6. Who was the only manager to win a pennant in both leagues?
7. What were the names of the clubs and their managers in the first season of the American League in 1901?
8. What was the Boudreau shift?
9. How was the shift beaten?
10. What team stole the most bases in a single season in the history of the game?
11. What team is credited with the most home runs during a single season?
12. What team won the most games during a single season?
13. What team lost the most games during a single season?

14. What team allowed the fewest runs on the average in a game?

15. What team pitched the most shutouts during a single season?

16. How many bases did the American League teams steal in 1912?

17. How many bases did the National League teams steal in 1911?

18. Who was the manager of the world champion Cincinnati Reds in 1919, the year of the Black Sox scandal?

19. Who managed the Black Sox?

20. In 1944 a once-powerful Yankee team was totally destroyed. What happened?

21. What players did the Yankees lose that year?

22. Who was the manager of the 1914 Miracle Braves?

23. Why was that team such a miracle?

24. How did Leo Durocher come about his famed line, "Nice guys finish last"?

25. Who were the Gas House Gang?

26. Name the players and their positions.

27. In 1961 the Chicago Cubs were placed on a unique coaching-managing system in hope of getting the club out of second division. What was that system?

28. What manager followed this system when it was abandoned two years later?

29. In 1912 the Detroit Tigers suffered from a team strike and had no players to face the Philadelphia Athletics. Why?

30. What happened?

31. In 1942 a St. Louis Cardinal manager

brought a team that had been pennantless for eight seasons into the winner's circle. Who?

32. What young rookie stars were members of that team?

33. Who was Cornelius Alexander McGillicuddy?

34. As a result of the player shortage of World War II, two handicapped players were signed by the American League to fill in. Who?

35. Who was Harry Steinfelt?

36. What famous infielder for the Chicago Cubs went on to greatness as manager of the Cubs later in his career?

37. Who were the Hitless Wonders?

38. What was their team batting average?

39. What team holds the record for the lowest team batting average for a season?

40. Who were the pitchers for the Hitless Wonders?

41. In 1953 a poll was taken to determine the greatest Yankee team of all time. What were the results of that poll?

42. What two colonels were credited with building the New York Yankee dynasty?

43. How much did they buy the Yankees for?

44. How much did they pay the Boston Red Sox for Babe Ruth?

45. What was the miracle of Coogan's Bluff?

46. What happened during the playoffs for the National League pennant in 1951?

47. In the early years of his managing career what team did Connie Mack manage?

48. What was the shot heard 'round the world?

49. What manager won three pennants with three different teams?

50. What Philadelphia Phillies player caused the firing and resignation of two managers?

51. In 1953 the owner of the St. Louis Cardinals was forced to sell his team, and to keep the club in St. Louis he sold it to one of the lower bidders. Who was he?

52. What bids did he turn down?

53. How did Cap Anson get himself fired as manager of the Chicago Colts?

54. What was the batting order for the New York Mets' first game on April 11, 1962?

55. What National League team threatened to strike a game against the Dodgers if Jackie Robinson was in the lineup?

56. Why wasn't Jackie Robinson brought up to the major leagues in 1946?

57. Who were the fielders for the Baltimore Orioles between 1892-1896?

58. What manager once ran a team of the day's greatest hitters for fourteen consecutive years and never won a world championship?

59. Why didn't he win a championship?

60. Give the lineups of the New York Yankees and New York Giants during the 1936 World Series.

61. Give the lineup of the 1930 Philadelphia Athletics.

62. Give the lineup of the 1927 New York Yankees.

63. Give the lineup of the 1955 Brooklyn Dodgers.

64. For the following managers, give the team he headed for the most years during his career.

    1. Bill Terry
    2. Danny Murtaugh
    3. Frank Selee
    4. Miller Huggins
    5. Walt Alston
    6. Ty Cobb
    7. Joe Cronin
    8. Pinky Higgins
    9. Red Schoendienst
    10. Charlie Grimm

65. What teams has Leo Durocher managed?

66. What teams did Casey Stengel manage?

67. For each of the following teams list the manager.

    1. 1946 Boston Braves
    2. 1969 Pittsburgh Pirates
    3. 1965 Cincinnati Reds
    4. 1948 Brooklyn Dodgers
    5. 1950 Philadelphia Athletics
    6. 1965 Chicago White Sox
    7. 1929 New York Yankees
    8. 1963 Washington Senators
    9. 1935 Detroit Tigers
    10. 1937 St. Louis Cardinals

68. During the 1947 season, with Leo Durocher suspended from the game, who managed the Brooklyn Dodgers?

69. What National League team is noted for the most innovations in the history of the sport?

70. What famed manager began his career in baseball as a means of paying his way through dental school?

71. Who was the most controversial manager the New York Yankees ever had?

72. What famous Yankee catcher later came out of retirement to work as a manager for that team?

73. What team has won more pennants, more World Series and had more record breaking players play for them than any other team on the American or National League?

74. What owner of a major league baseball team fired his manager and said he was going to manage the team himself? When did it happen?

Answers

1. For the first time the Amazing Mets did not end up in the cellar of the National League, finishing up the season in ninth place, ahead of Leo Durocher's Chicago Cubs. It was the first year the Yanks had been in the cellar in the American League since 1912, but in fairness to the Bronx Bombers, the Yanks did win more games that year than the Mets and did finish closer to first place in the American League than the Mets did in the National League.

2. 1966.

3. Stengel was replaced by Wes Westrum, who managed the Mets until the end of the 1967 season.

4. The scribe was Joe McCarthy, who managed in professional baseball for 24 years despite the fact that he had never played in the major leagues.

5. The Ten Commandments of Baseball.

    1. Nobody ever became a ballplayer by walking after a ball.

    2. You never will become a .300 hitter unless you take the bat off your shoulder.

    3. An outfielder who throws back of the runner is locking the barn after the horse is stolen.

4. Keep your head up and you may not have to keep it down.

5. When you start to slide, *slide*. He who changes his mind may have to change a good leg for a bad one.

6. Do not alibi on bad hops. Anybody can field the good ones.

7. Always run them out. You never can tell.

8. Do not quit.

9. Do not find too much fault with the umpires. You cannot expect them to be as perfect as you are.

10. A pitcher who doesn't have control doesn't have anything.

6. The "Old Engineer," as Joe McCarthy was called, gave the Chicago team a first and second place finish in the National League, the pennant win in 1929. With the Yankees from 1931 until 1946 he accumulated eight pennant wins in the American League.

7. Baltimore Orioles—John McGraw.
Boston Invaders—James Collins
Chicago White Sox—Clark Griffith
Cleveland Babes, Blue—James McAleer
Detroit Tigers—George Stallings
Milwaukee Brewers—Hugh Duffy
Philadelphia Athletics—Connie Mack
Washington Senators—James Manning

8. The Boudreau shift was a defensive play, devised by Cleveland Indian manager Lou Boudreau, that proved to be Ted Williams' nemesis during the 1946 seaon. Since Williams was a left-handed pull hitter, he usually hit most of his

long shots to right. Boudreau moved his four infielders to the right of second base and placed two of his three outfielders in right field, with the left-fielder stranded to protect the entire left of the field.

9. Williams finally beat the Boudreau shift in a close final game of the 1946 season. In a game against the Indians Williams slugged a late inning inside-the-park home run to bring the Bosox their first pennant in over 25 years.

10. The credit goes to the Philadelphia American Association team, which in 1887 stole a total of 638 bags in a single season.

11. The New York Yankees, with 240 in the 1961 season.

12. The Chicago Cubs in 1906, with 116 wins.

13. Cleveland in 1899 with 134 losses.

14. The Chicago Cubs in 1909, with an average of 2.4 runs per game.

15. The Chicago White Sox pitched a total of 32 shut outs.

16. In 1912 the American League stole 1,810 bases in a single season.

17. In 1911 the National League stole 1,691 bases. It was during that season that the New York Giants accumulated almost one-fifth of that total, with 347 bags. The Giants' chief base thieves were Artie Develin, Josh Devore, Charley Herzog, Fred Snodgrass and Fred Merkle.

18. Pat Moran.

19. Kid Gleason.

20. The World War II draft, which called up every able-bodied man in the country, left only overaged and physcially disqualified athletes to play in the major leagues. The draft hurt the world champion New York Yankees the most.

21. The same Yankee club that had clobbered the St. Louis Cardinals in the 1943 World Series by four games to one was wrecked by the draft, leaving Joe McCarthy with almost no material to work with. Bill Dickey, Spud Chandler, Joe Gordon, Charley Keller, Bill Johnson and Frank Crosetti were all inducted into the armed forces for the 1944 season. Although Crosetti returned to the Yanks halfway through the season, it was too late; the St. Louis Browns became the American League champs.

22. George Tweedy Stallings.

23. The cellar-dwelling Braves went on a winning streak in the middle of July, winning 61 of their last 77 games, finishing the season 10½ games ahead of all other teams. The Braves had started their streak 13 games behind the second place Giants.

24. Red Barber, the radio announcer, once asked Duroucher why he never was a nice guy, Duroucher laughed at the question and pointed out the Giants in the other dugout. "You know a nicer guy than Mel Ott?" he asked. Ott's club was then in eighth place. "All the Giants are nice guys. And see . . . nice guys finish last."

25. The Gas House Gang was the nickname for the 1934 St. Louis Cardinals.

26. Frankie Frisch (second base), Ducky Medwick (outfield), Pepper Martin (third base), Rip Collins (first base), J. Rothrock (outfield), Bill

Delancey (catcher), Leo Duroucher (shortstop), Ernie Orsatti (outfield), Dizzy Dean (pitcher), Paul Dean (pitcher).

27. During the season that Cubs abandoned the traditional managing system and began what was called the "college of coaches," a rotating staff with each coach allowed to head the team every fourth time. The system made no difference—the Cubs still had a losing season.

28. Bob Kennedy.

29. Ty Cobb had been suspended because he had gone into the stands during a game and beaten up a heckler. His teammates knew they didn't have a chance without him and went on strike.

30. Tiger manager Hugh Jennings had to scrape together a team to face the Philadelphia Athletics or face a possible $5,000 fine. Jennings collected a team of sandlot players, some Philadelphia semi-pro players and boys from St. Joseph's College to face Connie Mack's powerful club. Each player was paid ten dollars for his performance. The Tiger club was clobbered by the Athletics 24-2.

31. Billy Southworth, in one of the greatest comebacks of all time. With ten games behind Casey Stengel's Braves as late in the season as August 9, the Cardinal club kept winning until only a September 17 contest stood between them and victory. The Cards defeated the Braves in that final contest in a late inning rally, and went on to beat the New York Yankees in the World Series in five games.

32. Stan Musial, Terry Moore, Ernos Slaughter, Whitey Kurowski.

33. That unwieldy name was later reduced by this famed baseball immortal to simply Connie Mack, who for 50 years ran the Philadelphia Athletics. Mack and his team won the American League's pennant the second year of its existence in 1902 and followed through eight times in the next 30 years, with five of these pennant victories resulting in World Series championships.

34. The St. Louis Browns hired a rookie with only one arm to play the outfield. Pete Gray had a fine record with the Memphis club in the Southern Association the year before, slugging a .333 and stealing 68 bases. The Washington Senators hired Bert Shepard, who had been shot down while piloting a plane over Germany, to pitch despite the fact that he had only one leg.

35. Harry Steinfelt may never be remembered just because his name didn't fit into a rhyme. Steinfelt was the famed third baseman for the Chicago Cubs, part of that brilliant Chicago infield along with Frank Chance, Johnny Evers and Joe Tinker. Steinfeld was a solid fielder and hitter. He hit .471 during the 1907 World Series and led his league in RBIs in 1906. He finished that 1906 season with a .327 batting average.

36. Frank Chance managed the Chicago Cubs to four pennant victories during his years at the helm. Of those four pennants the Cubs won two world championships.

37. This is the name usually given to the 1906 Chicago White Sox, considered by some as a better team than the great and infamous 1919 Black Sox. The Hitless Wonders went on to win the

American League pennant in 1906 and defeated Frank Chance's great Chicago Cubs in the World Series.

38. They were the champions of the world with a lowly team batting average of .228.

39. The American Association Baltimore club back in 1886, with a team batting average of .204.

40. With absolutely no hitting, the Hitless Wonders had to rely primarily on its strong pitching staff. The team narrowly won 93 contests that year by as little as one run. Ed Walsh won 17 games that year, Doc White won 18, Frank Owen won 20 and Frank Patterson won 10.

41. In the outfield there was Babe Ruth, Joe DiMaggio and Bob Meusel. At first base the writers plugged in Lou Gehrig, at second base Tony Lazzeri and at third Red Rolfe. Phil Rizzuto was given the shortstop honors and Bill Dickey was called in to catch. Red Ruffing was chosen as the best right-handed pitcher and the left-handed honors were tied between Lefty Gomez and Herb Pennock. Johnny Murphy was given the relief pitching role.

42. A partnership between Colonel Jacob Ruppert and Colonel Tillinghast L'Hommedieu Huston bought the New York Highlanders, later to be known as the Yankees, in 1915.

43. They paid a reported sum of $450,000 for the team. $225 was paid in cash out of Colonel Huston's pocket the day of the arrangements.

44. The Red Sox were paid $125,000 for Babe Ruth.

45. The miracle began on August 11, 1951 when

the New York Giants, then under the directorship of Leo Durocher, were trailing their hometown rivals the Brooklyn Dodgers by 13½ games for the National League pennant. The Giants won the next 16 games in a row and finally, on the last day of the season, tied the Dodgers for the pennant title.

46. The Giants won the first playoff game with Jim Hearn pitching against the Dodger's Ralph Branca. The second game was won easily by the Dodgers with Clem Labine pitching a 10-0 shutout. Then came the final game of the playoffs. Sal Maglie was pitching for the Giants and Don Newcombe was on the mound for the Dodgers. Everything went down to the last inning with the Dodgers ahead 4-1. The Giants had won 38 of their last 46 games, 13 out of their last 15. Then came the shot heard round the world.

47. Mack began his career managing the Pittsburgh club in the National League. Under his direction the Pirates placed seventh in 1894 and sixth in 1895. He was released midseason in 1896.

48. This was the home run that decided the 1951 playoff between the Giants and Dodgers. Don Newcombe started the bottom of the ninth giving up hits to Alvin Dark and Don Mueller. Monte Irvin, up next, doubled, sending in Dark to score and bringing Mueller to third. This brought Bobby Thomson to the plate. And it was Thomson who put the topping on the miracle of Coogan's Bluff by drilling the second pitch into the left-field bleachers, bringing the Giants the National League pennant.

49. William Boyd McKechnie, known as

Deacon Bill, coached the Pittsburgh Pirates, St. Louis Cards and Boston Braves to pennant victories. The Pirates won the pennant and world championship in 1925. The St. Louis Cards won the pennant for McKechnie in 1928. The Cincinnati Reds won a pennant and world championship in 1940.

50. During the 1968 and 1969 seasons the Philadelphia Phillies went through two managers, Gene Mauch and Bob Skinner, because of personality conflicts they had with the team's star slugger Richie Allen. Mauch was fired by Bob Carpenter in 1968 and Skinner resigned in '69, claiming it was impossible to manage a ball club that Richie Allen played on.

51. Fred Saigh sold the St. Louis Cards to the Anheuser Busch Brewery for a reported $3,750,000.

52. Saigh turned down two higher offers from a Milwaukee group of businessmen and a Houston group.

53. After the Colts lost a close game in 1897 just because a base runner didn't feel like sliding, Anson announced publicly that his team "is composed of a bunch of drunkards and loafers who are throwing me down." The quote caused a furor throughout Chicago and Anson was subsequently fired by Colt boss James Hart.

54. Ashburn (centerfield), Mantilla (shortstop), Neal (second base), Thomas (leftfield), Bell (right field), Hodges (first base), Zimmer (third base), Landrith (catcher), Craig (pitcher).

55. The incident was officially called a "vicious rumor," but preceeding a St. Louis series with the

Dodgers at Ebbets Field in May, 1947, the Cardinal team had threatened to strike if the man to break baseball's color barrier walked on the field. The threat was eventually quashed by Ford Frick and club owner Sam Breadon.

56. The Dodger players decided themselves not to bring Robinson down from Montreal in 1946, even though he was slugging an impressive .340. The Dodgers needed his help in a heated battle for the pennant with the Cardinals, but some players had not yet been convinced to accept a Black player into their lineup.

57. Hanlon's fielders were Dan Brouthers at first, Kid Gleason at second, Hugh Jennings at short, John McGraw at third, Joe Kelly in left, Stevie Brodie in center, Willie Keeler in right and Wilbert Robinson catching.

58. Hugh Jennings, manager of the Detroit Tigers from 1907 until 1920, never had the good fortune of bringing his power-hitting club to the world championship circle. Although his team included such hitting greats as Ty Cobb, the Tigers never reached that much-coveted goal. Jennings brought the team three pennant wins in his first three years at the helm.

59. The Tigers, during those years, were up against some of the greatest teams of all time. The Tigers lost the 1907 bid to Frank Chance's Chicago Cubs. Ty Cobb hit a lowly .200 for the series, and the autumn games were lost 4-0-1. In 1908 the Tigers again lost four out of five games to the Cubs. And finally in 1909 they lost against the

Pittsburgh club that had won 110 games during the season.

60. New York Yankees (1936)
Frank Crosetti (ss)
Red Rolf (3b)
Joe DiMaggio (cf)
Lou Gehrig (1b)
Bill Dickey (c)
George Selkirk (rf)
John Powell (lf)
Tony Lazzeri (2b)

New York Giants
Joe Moore (lf)
Dick Bartell (ss)
Bill Terry (1b)
Hank Leiber (cf)
Mel Ott (rf)
Gus Mancuso (c)
Burgess Whitehead (2b)
Travis Jackson (3b)

61. Philadelphia Athletics (1930)
Max Bishop (2b)
Mule Haas (cf)
Mickey Cochrane (c)
Al Simmons (lf)
Jimmy Foxx (1b)
Bing Miller (rf)
Jimmy Dykes (3b)
Joe Boley (ss)

62. New York Yankees   (1927)
Earl Combs (cf)
Mark Koenig (ss)
Babe Ruth (rf)
Lou Gehrig (1b)
Bob Meusel (lf)
Tony Lazzeri (2b)
Joe Dugan (3b)
Benn Bengough (c)

63. Brooklyn Dodgers   (1955)
Pee Wee Reese (ss)
Junior Gilliam (2b)
Duke Snider (cf)
Jackie Robinson (3b)
Gil Hodges (1b)
Roy Campanella (c)
Carl Furillo (rf)
Sando Amoros (lf)

64.   1.   Billy Terry—New York Giants
     2.   Danny Murtaugh—Pittsburgh Pirates
     3.   Frank Selee—Boston Braves
     4.   Miller Huggins—New York Yankees
     5.   Walt Alson—Los Angeles Dodgers
     6.   Ty Cobb—Boston Red Sox
     7.   Joe Cronin—Boston Red Sox
     8.   Pinky Higgins—Boston Red Sox
     9.   Red Schoendienst—St. Louis Cardinals
   10.   Charlie Grimm—Chicago Cubs

65.   Brooklyn Dodgers, New York Giants, Chicago Cubs, Houston Astros.

66.   Brooklyn Dodgers, Boston Braves, New York

Yankees, New York Mets.
67. 1. Billy Southworth
      2. Bob Skinner
      3. Dick Sisler
      4. Burt Shotton
      5. Connie Mack
      6. Al Lopez
      7. Miller Huggins
      8. Gil Hodges
      9. Mickey Cochrane
     10. Frankie Frisch

68. Burt Shotton led Duroucher's Dodgers during that season to a National League pennant. Shotton often sat in the stands during the game, wearing his usual wire-rimmed spectacles and long coat. He had been Branch Rickey's Sunday manager for many years.

69. The Cincinnati Reds became the first professional team in 1869, the first team to own a farm system back in 1895, the first team to travel by airplane in 1934, the first team to play a World Series night game, the first team to play a televised game.

70. Casey Stengel began playing baseball in 1910 with the Kansas City Blues as a means of collecting enough money to pay his way through Western Dental College in Kansas City.

71. Billy Martin.

72. Yogi Bera.

73. The New York Yankees.

74. George Steinbrenner in 1980 when he fired Billy Martin.

Chapter Six

The World Series

It has been billed as the greatest annual event. Every year, the World Series games pack the stadiums and outdraw even the best films on television screens across America. It is the World Series that brings together the best of the National and American Leagues in a head-on confrontation to determine the best in the world.

To truly understand this annual autumn event, just think of the pictures you have seen after the last game, after that final out has been made and the winners and losers have left the stadium for their respective locker rooms. The winners with champagne bottles popping, chaos and celebration running rampant. The winning pitcher pulled into the shower. The home run slugger chugging down a bottle of Moët et Chandon. And then there are the losers, quietly packing their gear, thinking about what went wrong, what could have gone right. Already thinking about next season, when they can try once again.

The World Series has fostered some of the most exciting moments in the history of baseball. There was Don Larsen's perfect game in 1956. There was Pepper Martin doing everything right in 1931. There was the Babe's alleged called shot. And there were the Mets back in 1969. The World Series brings out the best in all players. There is an extra tension in the air that makes even the most confident pro want to out-hit, out-field, out-run and out-catch even his best performance. The winner's share of the money is only part of it. For most athletes it is a dream come true, the culmination of years of preparation and a year of hard playing. It is during the World Series that the best in baseball is decided. And the feeling of being the best, at least for one year, is enough reward in itself.

The World Series Quiz

1. What was the only World Series the Washington Senators ever won?

2. What was Walter Johnson's only World Series win?

3. What other time were the Senators in the World Series and what happened?

4. In the 1961 World Series between Cincinnati and New York, Whitey Ford broke Babe Ruth's most coveted record. What?

5. Who was Cookie Lavagetto?

6. For what is he most remembered?

7. Who were the Whiz Kids of 1950?

8. What were the results of the 1950 World Series?

9. What other team of Whiz Kids beat the Yankees in a five-game series, four games in a row?

10. What was the average age of that team and who was its oldest member?

11. Why wasn't there a 1904 World Series?

12. What pitcher never failed to lose a World Series game he started?

13. What manager decided to place Babe Ruth in the infield?

14. During the 45-year span between 1920 and 1965, how many American League pennants did the New York Yankees win?

15. What are the combined statistics for those teams?

16. What player-manager of the Cleveland Indians is credited with the team's pennant win and world championship in 1948?

17. In 1929 Connie Mack allowed a pitcher who had been fired earlier that season to start the first game of the World Series against the Chicago Cubs. Who?

18. How did he do?

19. Who played for more championship teams, Babe Ruth or Joe DiMaggio?

20. In what World Series did the losing team outscore the winning team by twice as many runs?

21. What was Elroy Face's record during the 1960 World Series?

22. What year did the Yankees beat the Cincinnati Reds in a World Series by four games in a row?

23. What happened during that year's World Series?

24. In 1966 the Boston Red Sox were in ninth place in the American League. In 1967 they were in the World Series. What two players made the difference?

25. What were these players' records during the 1967 World Series?

26. About what catcher did the mild-mannered Connie Mack once say he'd never seen such bad catching in a World Series game?

27. In what World Series were six out of the seven

games won by only one run?

28. What were the scores of those games?

29. Who is credited with winning the 1972 World Series for Oakland?

30. Who holds the World Series record for number of hits?

31. Who holds the World Series record for number of stolen bases?

32. Who holds the World Series record for highest-batting average?

33. Who holds the World Series record for number of wins?

34. Who holds the World Series record for number of losses?

35. Who holds the World Series record for number of at bats?

36. Who were the two teams that played the World Series in 1982?

37. Who won that series in 1982?

38. Who were the two teams that played the World Series in 1981?

39. Who won that series in 1981?

40. What year did the New York Yankees lose the first two games of the World Series and then come back and win 4 straight games to win the series?

41. Who were they playing against?

42. Who won the World Series 6 years in a row?

Answers

1. The big event came about at the end of the 1924 season in a full seven-game series against the New York Giants.

2. During the 1924 series Walter Johnson lost his first two starts but saved the day in the last game. He came to pitch in the late innings and held the Giants from scoring for four innings until the 12th, when Earl McNeely brought in Muddy Ruel on a ground ball, giving Johnson his only World Series win.

3. The Senators were in the World Series one other time: in 1933 against the Giants. They were beaten four games to one.

4. Ruth's record was established when he was a young southpaw pitching for the Boston Red Sox. In 1916 Ruth shut out the Dodgers for 13 innings, beginning his famed 29 2/3 innings of shut-out ball in World Series play. Whitey Ford brought this total of consecutive shut-out innings in World Series play up to 32 in the 1961 games. Ford had blanked the Pittsburgh Pirates in his two appearances in the 1960 World Series, and then came back in 1961 to shut out the Reds 2-0 in the first game of the series. Coming back to pitch in the fourth game, Ford pitched five shut-out innings before leaving the game because of an injured foot.

5. Cookie Lavagetto was a 34-year-old substitute third baseman who had recently come to the Brooklyn Dodgers before the 1947 World Series after three years with Pittsburgh. He had hit .300 only once in his career, back in 1939.

6. Lavagetto's big moment came when he pinch hit with two outs in the bottom of the ninth inning in the fourth game of the 1947 World Series between Brooklyn and the Yankees. Lavagetto slugged the ball against the right-field fence and two Dodger runners raced home to win the game.

7. The Whiz Kids were the Philadelphia Phillies of 1950, composed mostly of bonus babies like Mike Goliat, 24, at second base; Gran Hamner, 23, at shortstop; Willie Jones, 24, at third base; Del Ennis, 25, and Richie Ashburn, 23, both in the outfield; Robin Roberts, 23, and Curt Simmons, 21, pitching. The two old men of the team were Dick Sisler in the outfield and Andy Seminick, both 30 years old.

8. The Whiz Kids were soundly defeated that year by the New York Yankees in four straight games. By the end of that contest the Whiz Kids had scored five runs, of which only three were earned.

9. Eight years earlier a young Cardinal team, built out of youngsters because the team had lost many great players to the armed forces, beat the Yankees four in a row during the 1942 World Series. The team averaged only three years of professional experience.

10. The average age of that team was 26, and the oldest player was Terry Moore, the 30-year-old centerfielder.

11. The 1904 Boston Americans, still rolling after their victory in the first World Series in 1903, challenged John McGraw's Giants, the National League winner, to a series but McGraw declined, claiming, "They're nothing but a bunch of damn bush leaguers."

12. Babe Ruth pitched three games in the 1916 series and two in the 1918 contest, winning all five. Ruth went for 12 scoreless innings in the 1916 series in a 14-inning game which the Bosox finally won from the Brooklyn Dodgers, 2-1. During the 1918 series against Chicago Ruth won the first and fourth games and would have pitched a sixth had he not been taken out of the pitching rotation.

13. Ed Barrow.

14. During that period of time, often referred to as the Yankee Dynasty, the Bronx Bombers won 29 pennants in 45 years, beginning with their first in 1921 under the direction of Miller Huggins.

15. The Yanks slugged a total of 6,463 homers and had the highest team batting average. In addition the team made the most double plays and their pitchers were noted for the lowest ERA, 3.56.

16. They say that MVP player-manager Lou Boudreau did it all by himself that year.

17. A 35-year-old veteran named Howard Ehmke was chosen to start the first game of that year's series against the Chicago Cubs. Ehmke had been fired earlier that year because Mack had no need for him on a club that sported such pitching greats as George Earnshaw, Rube Waldberg, Jack Quinn and Ed Rommel. Ehmke had pitched only 55 innings that year and had won only seven games. That was the same season that Earnshaw had 24 wins, Grove had 20 and Walberg had 18. Ehmke, who had been with the team for 16 years, convinced Mack to keep him on to play on the first winning team in his career.

18. Ehmke, who was noted for his slow ball pitching, pitched shut-out ball against Chicago hitters like Rogers Hornsby, Kid Cuyler, and Hack Wilson. Ehmke struck out the side in the ninth inning, pitching a record of 13 strike outs, a record that stood for 24 years. The Athletics won the first game of that year's World Series 3-1. Ehmke was brought back to pitch in the final game of the series but was socked in the fourth inning with a double, a walk, and two singles, bringing in two runs. Walberg came in to pitch for him, finally winning the game in the ninth on an Athletic rally, 3-2.

19. If numbers of world championships is any indication, Joe DiMaggio's Yankee teams from 1936 until 1951 were better than the Babe's 1920-1934 teams. All in all Ruth played on seven pennant winners and four world championship teams during his Yankee career. DiMaggio played on ten pennant winners and nine world championship clubs in his 13 years with the Yankees.

20. Not only did the New York Yankees outscore the Pittsburgh Pirates during the 1960 World Series —and not only did the team hit .338 and slug in 91 hits and earn 55 runs, a World Series record— but they won three games by landslide victories: 16-3, 10-0, 12-0. The Pirates batted in only 27 runs during that series.

21. The major contributing factor to the Pirate victory was the pitching of Elroy Face, who brought three games—6-4, 3-2 and 5-2—to the Pittsburgh club.

22. In 1939 the Yankees swamped the Cincinnati Reds four games in a row for their fourth straight world championship.

23. The Yankees narrowly pulled off the first game, winning on a Bill Dickey hit in the bottom of the ninth, 2-1. The second game was a two-hit victory of the Yankees, 4-0. The third game was a slaughter. After the Reds socked a homer and three runs in the first inning, the Yankees came back with seven runs, including home runs by DiMaggio, Keller and Dickey, accounting for the Yanks' 7-3 victory. The fourth contest went to ten innings with the game tied 4-4. Eventually the game was won after Joe DiMaggio singled to right field, bringing in the winning run. Later that inning three more runs were scored, giving the Yankees the fourth game and world championship by a score of 7-4.

24. The two players were the 1967 Cy Young Award winner, Jim Lonberg, with a 22-9 record; and the team's 1967 Triple Crown winner, Carl Yastrzemski, who hit .326, and slugged in 121 runs and 44 home runs.

25. During that series Yaz hit three homers and batted .400. Lonberg won two games and lost one, but his two wins were a one-hit, 5-0 victory in the second game and a three-hit victory in the fifth game.

26. Yogi Berra, playing in the 1947 World Series

in his first season as a professional. During that series Berra had been stolen on seven times in just four games by Jackie Robinson and company. In addition he hit only .158 for the World Series competition. Berra came back to show how good he could be the next season, when he slugged .305 and drove in 98 runs.

27. It was during the 1972 World Series between Charley Finley's Oakland Athletics and the Cincinnati Reds that this World Series record was made.

28. The Oakland club picked up the first two games in Cincinnati, 3-2 and 2-1. The Reds won the third game 1-0 but lost the fourth 3-2, making the series three games to one. But then the Cincinnati club won the next two decisions, a 5-4 victory in the fifth game and in the sixth, 8-1, (the only game that wasn't decided by one run). The series was tied going into the seventh game; Oakland won the last game by a score of 3-2 and won the series.

29. It was in the seventh game that the A's catcher, Gene Tenace, came through in the clutch. Tenace drove home Angel Mangual with a single over the third-base line in the first inning. In the sixth inning Tenace doubled, driving in another run. Another double by Sal Bando drove in the winning run that gave the Oakland A's the championship. Despite the fact that he had hit only five home runs all season, Tenace hit four during the seven-game series, tying a record shared by Babe Ruth, Lou Gehrig and several others. In addition, Tenace accounted for nine of the Athletics' 16 runs during the series.

30. Yogi Berra with 71.
31. Lou Brock with 14.
32. Pepper Martin with .418.
33. Whitey Ford with 10.
34. Whitey Ford with 8.
35. Yogi Berra with 259.
36. The Milwaukee Brewers and the St. Louis Cardinals.
37. St. Louis won 4 games to 3.
38. The New York Yankees and the Los Angeles Dodgers.
39. Los Angeles—4 games to 2.
40. 1978.
41. The Los Angeles Dodgers.
42. The New York Yankees won from 1949-1954.

Great Moments in World
Series History Quiz

Fill in the blanks with the appropriate answer.

1. The 1932 World Series

It was a heated series that year, one with quite a bit of bench jockeying on both sides. One of the biggest targets of the National League pennant winner, the ____(1)____, was the New York Yankee's power hitter,____(2)____, who had been calling them cheapstakes because they had voted to give only a half share of the series winnings to ____(3)____, who had joined their club halfway through the season after leaving the Yankees.

So when ____(4)____ came up to bat in the ____(5)____ inning of the ____(6)____ game, the insults poured out of the National League pennant winner's dugout. ____(7)____pitched him ____(8)____ strikes and then the fans and every sportswriter at the game saw him point to ____(9)____field and then proceed to belt a home run into the stands.

Had he called his shots? No, say most players who were on the field that day. In fact, most players say he had been pointing at ____(10)____, who was playing____(11)____base and leading the heckling. ____(12)____ was scheduled to pitch the next day and later claimed that he heard ____(13)____yell at him, "You'll see tomorrow you bastard, we'll see what you can do with me." He then pointed to the pitching mound, in the direction of center field, where ____(14)____ would be pitching the next day.

Even though the shot might not have been called, the important fact was that it was ____ (15) ____'s last World Series home run, #____ (16) ____. The Yankees won the game that day by a score of ____ (17) ____.

2. The 1922 World Series

During the ____ (18) ____ game of a heated World Series between the ____ (19) ____ and the ____ (20) ____ the fans went wild. The game had gone into extra innings and even after ten both teams were still deadlocked by a score of ____ (21) ____. It was getting dark quickly and the game was suddenly called by the head umpire ____ (22) ____ at 4:45, even though there was at least a half hour of remaining daylight. His reasoning was that if the game continued it might continue into darkness or dusk and the players would have trouble following the ball.

The calling of the game drove the fans wild. They converged on the box of the commissioner of baseball ____ (23) ____ because they thought he was responsible. But he wasn't at all. In fact he was just as angry as the rest of the fans. After the game was called he ordered both teams to contribute the receipts from the first game to a war relief fund.

The next game was played in a drizzle and the field was a mess. It grew dark early, darker than it had been the day before when the game was called. But the game kept going until the ____ (24) ____ beat the ____ (25) ____, giving their manager, ____ (26) ____, his last World Series championship.

3. The 1948 World Series

The pressure had been on. Cleveland owner ____ (27) ____ was anxious to have a winner. The Indians hadn't won a pennant since ____(28)____. ____ (29) ____ had been acting as both player and manager for the past ____ (30) ____ years and things were beginning to look bad for his future if he didn't produce. But he did produce that year; whether it was luck or extra added pressure doesn't seem to matter.

For it was player-manager ____ (31) ____ who sparked the Indians' final drive for the pennant during the final months of 1948. He brought the team from ____ (32) ____ place and ____ (33) ____ games out of first at the beginning of September to first place by the final game of the season. All looked lost when they lost their final game to the ____ (34) ____. There was going to be a playoff between the Indians and the ____ (35) ____ for the American League pennant.

The ____ (36) ____ were then being led by their star slugger, ____ (37) ____, who had won that year's batting championship with a batting average of ____ (38) ____. But the Indians hadn't

139

give up yet. They gave it everything they had during the playoff. ____ (39) ____, a World War II Navy veteran and twenty-game winner that season, came through in the clutch to produce a ____ (40) ____-hit pitching performance. The runs were supplied by ____ (41) ____, who slugged ____ (42) ____ home runs and ____ (43) ____ singles, going four for four. The final score was ____ (44) ____.

But the bid for the championship was yet to come. The Indians had come from out of nowhere to play in the World Series. And they swept the series in ____ (45) ____ games against the National League pennant winners, the ____ (46) ____, even though the Indians' star hurler, ____ (47) ____, missed his chance to win his only World Series game, being beaten by the Braves' star hurler, ____ (48) ____.

4. The 1960 World Series

It was the ____ (49) ____ game of that year's contest that made all the difference in this, possibly the most unusual of all World Series. Neither starting pitchers went very far. Even the Pirates' star hurler, ____ (50) ____, couldn't stop the hard-hitting Yankee onslaught as they racked up ____ (51) ____ runs by the eighth inning. By then it looked like Yankee manager ____ (52) ____ had just picked up his ____ (53) ____ championship in ____ (54) ____ pennants. Then things began to change.

The Pirates had a runner on first at the bottom of the eighth with ____ (55) ____ up at bat. He pounded a routine grounder to Yankee short-stop ____ (56) ____. The play looked routine but the ball took a strange hop and hit ____ (57) ____ in the Adam's apple, getting ____ (58) ____ on the base and sending the Yankee short-stop to the hospital. ____ (59) ____ then singled and brought in a run, and ____ (60) ____ followed up by outrunning a short grounder to score another run. Catcher ____ (61) ____ looked like the hero of the game when he slugged a homer to bring the Pirates ahead by a score of ____ (62) ____. But the Yankees weren't world champions because they gave up easily. They tied the score in the top of the ninth. What happened in the bottom of the ninth inning made a man named ____ (63) ____ famous. He came up as the ____ (64) ____ batter in the bottom of the ninth. ____ (65) ____ was now pitching for the Yanks and he threw an inside pitch that he would regret for the rest of his life. The ball was powered over the left-field fence, giving the Pirates their first championship in ____ (66) ____ years.

5. The 1931 World Series

Whether or not Pepper Martin could have defeated the American League champion ____ (67) ____ single-handedly is doubtful, but the show he put on during that 1931 World Series is one of the most memorable ever by a single player.

The 1931 World Series was billed as the greatest contest of all time, bringing together the St. Louis Cardinals and the ____ (68) ____. Both teams had finished the season ____ (69) ____ ahead of the second place club in their respective leagues. The National League champions were being led by such greats as: ____ (70) ____, ____ (71) ____, ____ (72) ____, ____ (73) ____ and ____ (74) ____. Their opponents were no slouches either, led by such baseball greats as ____ (75)____, ____ (76) ____, ____ (77) ____ and ____ (78)____.

When the contest began on October 1, Pepper Martin showed right away who would be remembered most from that series. Although the ____ (79) ____ lost that first contest against ____ (80) ____'s mighty pitching, they slugged a total of ____ (81) ____ hits, losing by a score of ____ (82) ____. During that first game Martin hit two singles, a double and stole a base off the American League champion's might catcher, ____ (83) ____.

When the teams met again in the second game Martin did all the hitting while ____ (84) ____ pitched a brilliant three-hitter, shut-out victory, winning by a score of ____ (85) ____. During that game Martin ran to first on a routine base hit to center field but kept running, heading for second base. He beat out the throw. When the next pitch was thrown he took off again, stealing another base and putting himself in position to score on a fly ball by ____ (86) ____. Martin accounted for the second Cardinal run that game in the ____ (87) ____ inning. He singled, stole second and went to third on an infield out. He scored later that inning on a squeeze bunt by ____ (88) ____.

Martin came back in the third game, against the pitching of ____ (89) ____, and hit a single, a double and scored both times. The Cardinals beat the ____ (90) ____ this time by a score of ____ (91) ____.

Although the ____ (92) ____ won the fourth game, again by ____ (93) ____'s pitching performance, Martin got both hits against the pitcher, a single and double. He again stole a base off of the catcher, ____ (94) ____.

As if this weren't enough, his performance in the ____ (95) ____ game was possibly his finest. During that game Martin exploded with ____ (96) ____ big hits, one of which was a two-run homer. He accounted for four of the Cardinal's ____ (97) ____ runs that day.

After being left hitless in the ____ (98) ____ game against ____ (99) ____'s pitching performance, Martin came back in the final game to save the day, again hitting off ____ (100) ____. Martin had tied a major league World Series hitting record so far by tying ____ (101) ____ and ____ (102) ____'s record of ____ (103) ____ hits. But that day too Martin couldn't get a hit. He walked, struck out and grounded out. He got to first base once that day on an error made by ____ (104) ____. But it wasn't as a hitter that Martin made his mark that day. It was with his glove.

It happened in the bottom of the ____ (105) ____ inning with two outs and the tying runs on base for the ____ (106) ____. ____ (107) ____ popped a Texas Leaguer to center field. Martin could have let the ball drop, conceding one of the runs. Or he could have gone all or nothing and tried to catch the ball. He went for the catch. He raced in from center field and made a spectacular snag to end the series and to give the Cardinals the world championship.

Way back in 1981, the ____ (108) ____ and the ____ (109) ____ fought for the first time in a series. The ____ (110) ____ won the series in ____(111) ____ games to ____(112)____.

On October 8, 1915, the Philadelphia Phillies defeated the ____ (113) ____ 3-1 in the first game of the World Series. ____ (114) ____ years would go by before another pitcher Tug ____ (115) ____ would win the next world series for ____(116)____. That game was played in the year ____(117)____ against ____(118)____.

In 1982 the ____ (119)____ played ____(120) ____ and ____(121)____ won the series ____(122) ____ games to ____ (123) ____.

In the 1983 World Series the ____ (124) ____ won in ____ (125) ____ games to ____ (126) ____ over the ____ (127) ____. ____ (128) ____ pitched the winning game. Joe Morgan hit a home run in the ____ (129) ____ game while playing for ____ (130) ____. In game 3 ____ (131) ____ and ____ (132) ____ hit home runs while playing for the Phillies.

Answers

1. Chicago Cubs
2. Babe Ruth
3. Mark Koenig
4. Ruth
5. fifth
6. third game
7. Charlie Root
8. two strikes
9. center
10. Charlie Grimm
11. first base
12. Grimm
13. Ruth
14. Grimm
15. Ruth's
16. 15
17. 7-5
18. second
19. New York Giants
20. New York Yankees
21. 3-3
22. Bill Klem
23. Judge Landis
24. Giants

25. Yankees
26. John McGraw
27. Bill Veeck
28. 1920
29. Lou Boudreau
30. six
31. Boudreau
32. fourth
33. four and one-half
34. Detroit Tigers
35. Boston Red Sox
36. Boston Red Sox
37. Ted Williams
38. .369
39. Gene Beardan
40. five
41. Boudreau
42. two
43. two
44. 8-3
45. six
46. Boston Braves
47. Bob Feller
48. Johnny Sain
49. seventh
50. Elroy Face
51. seven
52. Casey Stengel
53. Eighth
54. ten
55. Bill Virdon
56. Tony Kubek
57. Kubek

58. Virdon
59. Dick Grote
60. Roberto Clemente
61. Hal Smith
62. 9-7
63. Bill Mazeroski
64. first
65. Ralph Terry
66. 35
67. Philadelphia Athletics
68. Athletics
69. 13
70. Chick Hafey
71. Jim Bottomley
72. Frankie Frisch
73. Bill Hallahan
74. Pepper Martin
75. Lefty Grove
76. Al Simmons
77. George Earnshaw
78. Mickey Cochrane
79. Cardinals
80. Lefty Grove
81. 12
82. 6-2
83. Mickey Cochrane
84. Hallahan
85. 2-0
86. Jim Wilson
87. seventh
88. Charley Gelbert
89. Lefty Grove
90. Athletics

91. 5-2
92. Athletics
93. Earnshaw
94. Cochrane
95. fifth
96. three
97. five
98. sixth
99. Lefty Grove
100. Earnshaw
101. Shoeless Joe Jackson
102. Sam Rice
103. 12
104. Jimmy Foxx
105. ninth
106. Athletics
107. Max Biship
108. Orioles
109. Pirates
110. Pirates
111. Four
112. Three
113. Boston Red Sox
114. 65
115. McGraw
116. Philadelphia
117. 1980
118. Kansas
119. Milwaukee Brewers
120. St. Louis Cardinals
121. St. Louis
122. 4
123. 3

124. Orioles
125. 4
126. 3
127. Philadelphia Phillies
128. Scott McGregor
129. 1st.
130. Philadelphia Phillies
131. Gary Mathews
132. Joe Morgan

World Series Results 1903-1983
(winner listed first)

1903 Boston (American League) versus Pittsburgh (National League). Final Score: 5 games to 3 games.

1905 New York (National) versus Philadelphia (American). Final Score: 4-1

1906 Chicago (American) versus Chicago (National). Final Score: 4-2

1907 Chicago (National) versus Detroit (American). Final Score: 4-0

1908 Chicago (National) versus Detroit (American). Final Score: 4-1

1909 Pittsburgh (National) versus Detroit (American). Final Score: 4-3

1910 Philadelphia (American) versus Chicago (National). Final Score: 4-1

1911 Philadelphia (American) versus New York (National). Final Score: 4-2

1912 Boston (American) versus New York (National). Final Score: 4-3

1913 Philadelphia (American) versus New York (National). Final Score: 4-1

1914 Boston (National) versus Philadelphia (American). Final Score: 4-0

1915 Boston (American) versus Philadelphia (National). Final Score: 4-1
1916 Boston (American) versus Brooklyn (National). Final Score: 4-1
1917 Chicago (American) versus New York (National). Final Score: 4-2
1918 Boston (American) versus Chicago (National). Final Score: 4-2
1919 Cincinnati (National) versus Chicago (American). Final Score: 5-3
1920 Cleveland (American) versus Brooklyn (National). Final Score: 5-2
1921 New York (National) versus New York (American). Final Score: 5-3
1922 New York (National) versus New York (American). Final Score: 4-0
1923 New York (American) versus New York (National). Final Score: 4-2
1924 Washington (American) versus New York (American). Final Score: 4-3
1925 Pittsburgh (National) versus Washington (American). Final Score: 4-3
1926 St. Louis (National) versus New York (American). Final Score: 4-3
1927 New York (American) versus Pittsburgh (National). Final Score: 4-0
1928 New York (American) versus St. Louis (National). Final Score: 4-0
1929 Philadelphia (American) versus Chicago (National). Final Score: 4-1
1930 Philadelphia (American) versus St. Louis (National). Final Score: 4-0
1931 St. Louis (National) versus Philadelphia

(American). Final Score: 4-0

1932 New York (American) versus Chicago (National). Final Score: 4-0

1933 New York (National) versus Washington (American). Final Score: 4-1

1934 St. Louis (National) versus Detroit (American). Final Score: 4-3

1935 Detroit (American) versus Chicago (National). Final Score: 4-2

1936 New York (American) versus New York (National). Final Score: 4-2

1937 New York (American) versus New York (National). Final Score: 4-1

1938 New York (American) versus Chicago (National). Final Score: 4-0

1939 New York (American) versus Cincinnati (National). Final Score: 4-0

1940 Cincinnati (National) versus Detroit (American). Final Score: 4-3

1941 New York (American) versus Brooklyn (National). Final Score: 4-1

1942 St. Louis (National) versus New York (American). Final Score: 4-1

1943 New York (American) versus St. Louis (National). Final Score: 4-1

1944 St. Louis (National) versus St. Louis (American). Final Score: 4-2

1945 Detroit (American) versus Chicago (National). Final Score: 4-3

1946 St. Louis (National) versus Boston (American). Final Score: 4-3

1947 New York (American) versus Brooklyn (National). Final Score: 4-3

1948 Cleveland (American) versus Boston (National). Final Score: 4-2

1949 New York (American) versus Brooklyn (National). Final Score: 4-1

1950 New York (American) versus Philadelphia (National). Final Score: 4-0

1951 New York (American) versus New York (National). Final Score: 4-2

1952 New York (American) versus Brooklyn (National). Final Score: 4-3

1953 New York (American) versus Brooklyn (National). Final Score: 4-2

1954 New York (National) versus Cleveland (American). Final Score: 4-0

1955 Brooklyn (National) versus New York (American). Final Score: 4-3

1956 New York (American) versus Brooklyn (National). Final Score: 4-3

1957 Milwaukee (National) versus New York (American). Final Score: 4-3

1958 New York (American) versus Milwaukee (National). Final Score: 4-3

1959 Los Angeles (National) versus New York (American). Final Score: 4-2

1960 Pittsburgh (National) versus New York (American). Final Score: 4-3

1961 New York (American) versus Cincinnati (National). Final Score: 4-1

1962 New York (American) versus San Francisco (National). Final Score: 4-3

1963 Los Angeles (National) versus New York (American). Final Score: 4-0

1964 St. Louis (National) versus New York

(American). Final Score: 4-3

1965 Los Angeles (National) versus Minnesota (American). Final Score: 4-3

1966 Baltimore (American) versus Los Angeles (National). Final Score: 4-0

1967 St. Louis (National) versus Boston (American). Final Score: 4-3

1968 Detroit (American) versus St. Louis (National). Final Score: 4-3

1969 New York (National) versus Baltimore (American). Final Score: 4-1

1970 Baltimore (American) versus Cincinnati (National). Final Score: 4-1

1971 Pittsburgh (National) versus Baltimore (American). Final Score: 4-3

1972 Oakland (American) versus Cincinnati (National). Final Score: 4-3

1973 Oakland (American) versus New York (National). Final Score: 4-3

1974 Oakland (American) versus Los Angeles (National). Final Score: 4-1

1975 Cincinnati (National) versus Boston (American). Final Score: 4-3

1976 Cincinnati (National) versus New York (American). Final Score: 4-0

1977 New York (American) versus Los Angeles (National). Final Score: 4-2

1978 New York (American) versus Los Angeles (National). Final Score: 4-2

1979 Baltimore (American) versus Pittsburgh (National). Final Score: 4-3

1980 Kansas City (American) versus Philadelphia (National). Final Score: 4-2

1981 New York (American) versus Los Angeles
      (National). Final Score: 4-2
1982 Milwaukee (American) versus St. Louis
      (National). Final Score: 4-3
1983 Baltimore (American) versus Philadelphia
      (National). Final Score: 4-1

Chapter Seven

One for the Record Books

Through baseball's long history it has been the record books that have maintained the achievements of all the great players. The record books have maintained the level of excellence for which all hitting, pitching and fielding stars must strive. Some of these records resulted from a fluke: a player who had never done anything out of the ordinary one day breaks a much heralded record or two. Some of these records are not always distinguished—a pitcher who walked the most batters, a fielder who dropped the most balls. And then there are records that many never believed breakable. For years the number 714 was a magical figure that most never thought could be reached until Hank Aaron shattered that legendary mark. Other records have been broken without nearly as much fanfare. And some records, especially those in the area of fielding averages, pinch hitting

157

and relief pitching, are usually ignored altogether.

That is unless you are truly a baseball scholar with a computerized memory and calculator reflexes. Records are broken in the sport of baseball yearly and it would take a mathematical wizard to be able to have such instant recall to remember what the record for the most double plays in a career by a shortstop is. Lifetime batting averages are a little easier to remember. But for the real hard core baseball fans even the most obscure statistics might not be too obscure to be remembered. So as a short test to see how good you are at remembering records, give the following Statistics Game a try. All records are as of the 1975 season and most likely will change as time goes on. As has always been said, records are made to be broken, and as long as baseball continues at the present level it seems like this old adage will still apply.

The Statistic Game

1. What pitcher has the lowest career earned run average?

    a.   Lefty Grove
    b.   Bob Gibson
    c.   Ed Walsh
    d.   Walter Johnson

2. What pitcher walked the most batters in his career?

    a.   George Earnshaw
    b.   Early Wynn
    c.   Whitey Ford
    d.   Roger Craig

3. What batter once hit seven consecutive hits in a single game?

    a.   Roger Maris
    b.   Cesar Gutierrez
    c.   Pat Dobson
    d.   Stan Musial

4. Who holds the record for the most consecutive games played in the National League?

    a.   Rogers Hornsby
    b.   Roberto Clemente
    c.   Billy Williams
    d.   Eddie Mathews

5. What relief pitcher won and saved the most games in his career?

    a. Hoyt Wilhelm
    b. Roy Face
    c. Bob Locker
    d. Joe McGinnity

6. What pitcher struck out the most batters in a single season?

    a. Rube Waddell
    b. Bob Feller
    c. Sandy Koufax
    d. Nolan Ryan

7. What batter was struck the most times by pitches during his career?

    a. Mel Ott
    b. Pepper Martin
    c. Ron Hunt
    d. Tony Oliva

8. What pitchers had thrown two no-hitters in a single season?

    a. Sandy Koufax, Cy Young, Rube
        Waddell, Warren Spahn
    b. Johnny Vander Meer, Jim Maloney,
        Virgil Trucks, Nolan Ryan, Allie
        Reynolds
    c. Robin Roberts, Jim Bunning,
        Whitey Ford, Bob Gibson

9. What player twice stole six bases during a regular nine-inning game?

    a. Eddie Collins
    b. Maury Wills
    c. Lou Brock
    d. Ty Cobb

10. What batter hit home runs in eight consecutive games?

    a.   Babe Ruth

    b.   Yogi Berra

    c.   Johnny Mize

    d.   Dale Long

11. List the batters who have hit over 50 homers in either a 154-game or 162-game schedule.

12. When was the first recorded no-hit game pitched?

13. What batter was walked the most times in his career?

    a.   Lou Gehrig

    b.   Babe Ruth

    c.   Roger Maris

    d.   Mickey Mantle

14. What batter struck out the most times in his career?

    a.   Ron Swoboda

    b.   Babe Ruth

    c.   Willie Mays

    d.   Mickey Mantle

15. What batter holds the record for the highest career batting average?

16. What year did Don Cardwell, Lew Burdette and Warran Spahn all throw a no-hit game?

17. Who holds the record for the most doubles hit during his career?

    a.   Roberto Clemente

    b.   Ty Cobb

    c.   Rogers Hornsby

    d.   Tris Speaker

18. Who holds the record for the most triples hit

during his career?

    a.   Ty Cobb
    b.   Tris Speaker
    c.   Sam Crawford
    d.   Willie McCovey

19. Who holds the record for the most RBIs in a single season?

    a.   Chuck Klein
    b.   Hank Greenberg
    c.   Hack Wilson
    d.   Willie Mays

20. What second baseman holds the record for the highest fielding percentage in a single season of play?

    a.   Bobby Richardson
    b.   Rogers Hornsby
    c.   Red Schoendienst
    d.   Jerry Adair

21. What pitcher holds the record for the highest season's fielding average?

    a.   Don Drysdale
    b.   Catfish Hunter
    c.   Larry Jackson
    d.   Al Jackson

22. What batter holds the record for the most hits in a single season of play?

    a.   Ty Cobb
    b.   George Sisler
    c.   Rogers Hornsby
    d.   Jackie Robinson

23. Who holds the record for being struck out the most times in a single season?

    a.   Bobby Bonds

     b.   Hank Aaron

     c.   Reggie Jackson

     d.   Babe Ruth

24. Who holds the record for the highest batting average during a single season of play?

     a.   Hugh Duffy

     b.   George Wright

     c.   Rogers Hornsby

     d.   Nap Lajoie

25. What shortstop holds the record for the most double plays made during a single season?

     a.   Pee Wee Reese

     b.   Phil Rizzuto

     c.   Lou Boudreau

     d.   Bobby Wine

26. During 1969 what pitchers threw no-hitters?

27. What pitcher threw the most complete games during his career?

     a.   Kid Nichols

     b.   Amos Rusie

     c.   Cy Young

     d.   Warren Spahn

28. Who holds the record for the most pinch hits?

     a.   Gene Woodling

     b.   Smokey Burgess

     c.   Orlando Cepeda

     d.   Manny Moto

29. Name the five runners to have stolen the most bases during their career.

30. Name the ten batters to have hit the most home runs during their career.

31. Which batter had the most at bats during a single season of play?

a. Willie Wilson
b. Pete Rose
c. Joe DiMaggio
d. Ted Williams

32. What third baseman made the most career double plays?

a. Jimmy Collins
b. Pinky Higgins
c. Ken Boyer
d. Brooks Robinson

33. What batter struck out the fewest times per times at bat?

a. Phil Rizzuto
b. Willie Keeler
c. Joe Sewell
d. Lave Cross

34. In 1968 what batter hit ten home runs in six consecutive games?

35. What catcher holds the record for the most double plays during his career?

a. Ray Schalk
b. Elston Howard
c. Gabby Hartnett
d. Mickey Cochrane

36. Who was the American League player who came to bat 705 times in a single season?

37. In what year did he accomplish this feat?

38. Who had the most steals for the Texas Rangers in 1978?

39. Who has the record for the most shutouts in baseball history and in what year and what team was he playing for?

40. Who got the most doubles in a single season?

Answers

1. Ed Walsh, with a lifetime total average of 1.82.

2. Early Wynn, who walked a total of 1775 batters in his lifetime career of 23 years.

3. Cesar Gutierrez pulled this off while playing shortstop for the Detroit Tigers back in 1970. This feat had happened only once before in the history of the game—back in 1892, when Wilbert Robinson hit seven hits for the Baltimore club.

4. Billy Williams, then playing for the Chicago Cubs, played for 1117 games in a row in 1970.

5. Hoyt Wilhelm played 21 years for the New York Giants, Baltimore Orioles, Chicago White Sox, and Los Angeles Dodgers, and won and saved 350 games pitching relief.

6. Nolan Ryan, who had just moved west to play with the California Angels, struck out 383 batters during the 1973 season to beat out Sandy Koufax's 1965 total of 382 strikeouts.

7. Ron Hunt holds this dubious distinction, having been hit 50 times during his major league career.

8. Johnny Vander Meer, Jim Malone, Virgil Trucks, Nolan Ryan and Allie Reynolds all threw

two no-hitters in a single season.
9. Eddie Collins.
10. In 1956 Dale Long, playing for the Pittsburgh Pirates, went on a home run hitting spree that lasted eight consecutive games.
11.   Roger Maris (61), 1961
        Mickey Mantle (54), 1961
        Babe Ruth (60), 1927
        Babe Ruth (59), 1921
        Jimmy Foxx (58), 1921
        Ralph Kiner (54), 1949
        Johnny Mize (51), 1947
        Ralph Kiner (51), 1947
        Hank Greenberg (58), 1930
        Willie Mays (51), 1955
        Jimmy Foxx (50), 1938
        Lewis Wilson (56), 1930
        Babe Ruth (54), 1920
        Babe Ruth (54), 1928
21. George Bradley pitched the first no-hit game on record on July 15, 1876.
13. Babe Ruth was walked the most times during his career, with a total of 2056 free rides to first. Ted Williams comes a close second with 2019 bases on balls.
14. The mighty Yankee switch hitter, Mickey Mantle, struck out the most times during his career with 1710.
15. Ty Cobb, with a lifetime batting average of .369.
16. 1960. Cardwell (May 15), Lew Burdette (August 18), Warren Spahn (September 15).
17. During his 22 years playing outfield for the

American League, Tris Speaker socked 793 doubles.

18. During his 19 years, mostly with the Detroit Tigers, Sam Crawford hit 312 doubles.

19. During the 1930 season, while playing for the Chicago Cubs, Hack Wilson hit 190 RBIs.

20. Jerry Adair of the Baltimore Orioles had a .994 fielding average during the 1964 season.

21. Out of 109 chances, Larry Jackson of the Chicago Cubs didn't make one error, fielding 1,000 for the 1964 season.

22. In 1920 George Sisler of the St. Louis Browns hit 257 hits.

23. In 1970 Bobby Bonds, then of the San Francisco Giants, struck out 189 times, beating his 1967 mark of 187 strike outs.

24. If you're counting as far back as 1894, Hugh Duffy of the Boston club has this mark with a .438 batting average. If you're talking about modern times, Rogers Hornsby holds the record with .424 during the 1924 season.

25. Bobby Wine, at shortstop for the Montreal Expos, made 137 double plays in the 1970 season.

26. Bill Stoneman (7-0) for Montreal
Bob Moose (4-0) for Pittsburgh
Don Wilson (4-0) for Houston
Jim Maloney (1-0) for Cincinnati
Ken Holtzman (3-0) for the Chicago Cubs

27. The immortal Cy Young threw 756 complete games during his career in the major leagues.

28. Smokey Burgess hit 145 pinch hits during his 18 years catching for both National and American League teams.

29. Lou Brock, Max Carey, Ty Cobb, Eddie Collins, Honus Wagner.

30. Hank Aaron, Ernie Banks, Jimmy Foxx, Harmon Killebrew, Mickey Mantle, Eddie Mathews, Willie Mays, Babe Ruth, Frank Robinson, Ted Williams.

31. Willie Wilson, batting for Kansas City came up to bat 705 times in a single season.

32. Brooks Robinson of the St. Louis Cardinals holds the record for the most career double plays for a third baseman, with 531 by the end of the 1973 season.

33. During his 14-year career with the Cleveland Indians and the New York Yankees, Joe Sewell only struck out .016 of the times he came up to bat.

34. During the 1968 season Frank Howard of the Washington Senators hit ten home in six consecutive games.

35. Ray Schalk has a career total of 221 double plays as a catcher for the Chicago White Sox and New York Giants.

36. Willie Wilson of Kansas City.

37. 1980.

38. Bump Wills

39. In 1916 Grover C. Alexander pitched 16 shutouts while playing for Philadelphia.

40. In 1931 Earl W. Webb got 67 doubles in a single season while playing for Boston.

Chapter Eight

Know the Rules

If Albert Spalding and other founding fathers of the sport of baseball were around today, they'd hardly recognize the sport that they helped found and build into our nation's favorite pastime. Not only has the sport grown by leaps and bounds since the early days of the twentieth century, but the rules have also changed in order to adapt to the new types of players that have been attracted to the sport. It has always been the desire of those in charge of baseball to make it as fair a sport as possible. The rules have been continually changed and newly adopted to try to negotiate a respectable similarity on the part of batters, pitchers and fielders.

In order to test how much you know about the rules and the development of the rules of the game of baseball, try your hand at the following Rulebook Quiz. Be careful, since many of the rules have changed several times during the history of the game.

Rulebook Quiz

1.   Is an error charged to the catcher on a base on balls?

2.   Is a bunt that goes foul considered a strike on the batter?

3.   What is the maximum diameter of the bat?

4.   How many innings must a pitcher pitch in order to be eligible as an ERA leader in his league?

5.   How many times at bat must a batter have to be eligible to lead the league with a batting average?

6.   What is the minimum distance along the foul line for a professional stadium?

7.   What is the minimum distance from home plate to the center-field fence?

8.   What is a rookie?

9.   What is the strike zone?

10.   Can someone pinch hit for the designated hitter?

11.   How high is the pitchers mound?

12.   What year was the spitball ruling?

13.   Is the pitcher given a strike out if he throws the batter a third strike and the catcher drops it, allowing the batter to get on first?

14.   If a batter strikes out after bunting on a third

strike, who is credited with the put out?

15. Is a base on balls credited as a hit? A time at bat?

16. How is an earned run scored?

17. During a double steal, if one of the runners is caught out, is the other still credited with a stolen base?

18. When a runner is struck by a batted ball who is given credit for the put out?

19. Is the designated hitter eligible for any batting titles?

20. What is the ground-rule double ruling?

21. What year was the American League batting title not given to the batter with the highest percentage?

22. Is a batter given an RBI if a runner scores despite the fact that he hit into a double play?

23. What year did the distance between home plate and the pitcher's box change?

24. What are the dimensions of the pitcher's box?

25. Does a bat have to be round?

26. When was the latest amendment to the designated hitter rule?

27. The strike zone is to include the area from the top of the shoulder to the bottom of the knee. When was this rule adopted?

28. An earned run is a run scored by the aid of hits only. When was this rule adopted?

Answers

1. No.

2. Yes.

3. In 1895 it was decided that the maximum diameter of the bat has to be 2 3/4 inches.

4. To be eligible as a league leader for earned run averages, a pitcher has to pitch a minimum of one inning per scheduled game. Previously the rule had read that a pitcher had to pitch a minimum of ten full games and 100 innings to qualify.

5. A batter must go to the plate at least 3.1 times for each game in order to qualify as a contender for his league's batting average crown.

6. In 1959 it was decided that the minimum distance between home plate and the outfield fence along either foul line has to be a minimum of 325 feet.

7. 400 feet.

8. In 1971 the official Major League Scoring Committee ruled that the following qualifications must be met by any young player to be considered a rookie: no more than 50 innings pitched, no more than 130 at bats, no more than 45 days on a major league team between the start of the season to the end of August.

9.   This is a ruling that has changed many times throughout the history of baseball. In the 1950s the strike zone was considered to be the area between the top of the batter's knee and his armpits. This was later changed in 1963 to include the area between the batter's shoulder to the bottom of the knee. Most recently the strike zone has again been limited to the area between the top of the knee and the armpits.

10.   Yes. But the pinch hitter for the designated hitter then becomes the official designated hitter for that game. The original designated hitter can no longer come back into the game.

11.   The height of every pitcher's mound in both leagues cannot be over ten inches higher than any other point on the field.

12.   The original spitball ruling came about in the 1920 season. It was originally ruled that each team could keep only two official spitballs until the end of that season, but that would be it. This was later amended in 1921 so that the National League could retain eight spitball pitches and the American League retain nine until the ends of those pitchers' careers.

13.   No.

14.   The catcher.

15.   No.

16.   The only way for a run to be officially considered "earned" is when it is scored as a result of a hit.

17.   No.

18. The fielder nearest him.

19. According to the ruling as designed in 1973, a designated hitter is able to pursue any league batting title that there is.

20. This ruling applies to any ball that somehow ends up outside of the playing field after first bouncing on the field.

21. In 1938 Jimmy Foxx was given the American League batting title despite the fact that Taffy Wright had a higher batting average. Wright, outfielder for the Washington Senators, batted a .350 average with 92 hits in 263 at bats. Foxx, on the other hand, hit .349 with 197 hits in 565 at bats. Wright had appeared in 100 games that year, as per the official ruling.

22. No.

23. The original change in this dimension occurred in 1881, when the distance changed from 45 feet to 50 feet. The measurement changed again in 1893, to 60 feet 6 inches.

24. 4 feet by 5½ feet.

25. Previous to 1893 a portion of every bat could be flat. This ruling was changed in 1893, and the bat must be totally round.

26. December 5, 1978.

27. 1963.

28. 1897.

Bibliography

Title	Publisher	Copyright Date
The Sporting News Official Baseball Guide	The Sporting News	1982
The History of National League Baseball	Stein & Day	1979
The Image of Their Greatness	Crown, Inc. N.Y.	1979
Yankees An Illustrated History	Prentice-Hall, Inc.	1982
Reggie Jackson's Scrapbook	Windmill Books and E.P. Dutton, N.Y.	1978
The New York Yankees	Crown Publishers, Inc., N.Y.	1982
American League Baseball		
The Baseball Encyclopedia	Macmillan Pub. Co.	1982
The Complete Handbook of Baseball	The New American Library, NY	1983

The Guiness Book of World
Records 1982-83

The World Encyclopedia

Sports Illustrated Book
of World Records

505 Questions on Baseball   Walker Pub. Co.   1980

Famous First Facts 4th Ed.

The Bill James Baseball
Abstract   Ballantine Books,NY   1982

Sporting News Baseball
Record Book

Official Baseball Dope Book

The History of American
League Baseball   Stein and Day   1980

The World Series   Rand McNally & Co.   1981

*Questions have been double-checked by The Baseball Hall of
Fame.